The Complete
No-Check
Low-Check

What's Inside

Welcome to the complete
No-Check
Low-Check

Our three No-Check Low-Check books have proved so popular, we have put them all together in this bumper edition packed full of recipes to help you make full use of No-Check foods, Every Day Bonus foods and other foods which have a low Check value.

You'll find lots of tasty ideas that can be eaten at any time as long as, on average, you keep within your daily Checks allowance.

Although most of us try to stick to a regular routine when trying to lose weight, there are often occasions when we may need to cut back a little –

KEY
to the symbols
used in this book

Calories → **150** Checks **6** **1** → Fat Grams

All values exclude "No-Check" foods which do not need to be counted.

If you are trying to save Checks for a special social occasion, these recipes provide nutrition and satisfaction but make it easy to save.

Had a bad day or two? There's no need to starve in order to try and compensate. Just make yourself a couple of nice low-Check meals, then get back to your usual weight loss routine.

These recipes may be low on Checks, but they're high on taste, nutrition and satisfaction. You can be reassured that many of the foods used – such as vegetables, fruit, lean meat and fish – are packed full of beneficial nutrients that can help you feel good whilst doing you a power of good.

We've also included lists of No-Check and Low-Check basic foods ideal for using in your own healthy meal ideas. Losing weight, and keeping it off, will be much easier if you get to know these foods well and build meals around them.

Positive Eating allows for the fact that "No-Check" foods do contain a few calories, but we've taken them into account when recommending daily Check allowances. So, as far as you're concerned, if it has "No-Check" value, you don't need to count it!

No-Check
Soups

Chinese Mushroom & Water Chestnut Soup

Serves 2 to 3

- 600 ml/1 pint chicken stock
- 1 small red chilli, finely sliced
- 1 cm/½ inch piece fresh root ginger, peeled and grated
- 1 lemon grass stalk, bruised with a knife
- Few drops of light soy sauce or nam pla (Thai fish sauce)
- Spray oil
- 175 g/6 oz shiitake mushrooms, sliced
- Handful of shredded greens, e.g. cabbage, spring greens, pak choi, spinach
- 2 spring onions, shredded
- 115 g/4 oz canned water chestnuts, drained and sliced
- Salt and pepper

Pour the chicken stock into a saucepan and bring to the boil.

Add the chilli, ginger and lemon grass and simmer gently for about 15 minutes, until the liquid is well flavoured. Add soy sauce or nam pla to taste.

Meanwhile, lightly spray a small pan with oil and cook the mushrooms until golden.

Add them to the soup with the shredded greens, spring onions and water chestnuts, and cook gently for 2-3 minutes, until the greens have softened.

Remove the lemon grass, check the seasoning and serve very hot.

No-Check

Spring Green Soup

Serves 4

INGREDIENTS

115g/4 oz leek
1200ml/2 pints mild vegetable stock
115g/4 oz courgette, thinly sliced
115g/4 oz savoy cabbage, finely shredded
Black pepper

tip:
To shred cabbage finely, remove tough stalks and lay leaves on top of each other. Roll-up like a fat cigar and cut thin slices.

Wash leek thoroughly and slice finely, including some of the green.

Put stock into a large saucepan, bring to the boil and add all the vegetables. Bring back to a simmer and cook approximately 3-5 minutes or until vegetables are just tender.

Season with black pepper.

No-Check

Leek, Courgette & Celery Soup

Serves 4

INGREDIENTS

1 large leek
2 medium courgettes
2 celery stalks
900 ml/1½ pints chicken or vegetable stock
1 tbsp fresh chopped parsley
Salt and pepper

Wash and trim the leek and cut into thick slices. Trim and slice the courgettes. Trim and finely slice the celery stalks.

Place all the vegetables in a large saucepan together with the stock. Bring to the boil, then lower the heat, cover and simmer approximately 15 minutes, stirring occasionally.

Stir in the parsley and season to taste.

Marrow & Mint Soup

Serves 3 to 4

INGREDIENTS

1 medium marrow, peeled, de-seeded and chopped
1 medium onion, chopped
Good handful fresh mint leaves
2 Oxo vegetable cubes
600ml/1 pint hot water

Place marrow, onions and mint in a large saucepan. Dissolve vegetable cubes in hot water and add to pan. Bring to a simmer, cover and cook approximately 15 minutes, or until vegetables are soft.

Allow to cool a little and liquidise for just a few seconds. Re-heat as necessary.

Broccoli & Tarragon Soup

Serves 4

Courtesy of member Bernadine Dooley, Clydebank

INGREDIENTS

2 medium onions, chopped
2 cloves garlic, crushed
Spray oil
450g/1lb broccoli florets
1 tbsp fresh tarragon leaves or 1 tsp dried
1 bay leaf
600ml/1 pint vegetable stock

Put onions and garlic into a large oil-sprayed saucepan. Cover and cook gently about 10 minutes until softened. Stir occasionally and add a little water if necessary to prevent sticking.

Add broccoli, tarragon, bay leaf and stock, bring to a simmer, cover and cook until all ingredients are soft.

Allow to cool a little, remove bay leaf and liquidise. Re-heat as necessary.

tip:
For a special treat, swirl 1 tbsp white wine into each serving, adding just half a Check!

Chicken & Celery Soup

Serves

INGREDIENTS

1 Oxo chicken cube
300ml/½ pint water
1 large stick celery, finely sliced

Crumble cube into a small saucepan, add water and bring to the boil, stirring until cube has dissolved.

Add celery and simmer approximately 15 minutes or until tender. Add more water, if liquid reduces too much.

Celery & Onion Soup

Serves **3** to **4**

Courtesy of class manager Diane Marlee

INGREDIENTS

Spray oil
1 head of celery, chopped
2 medium onions, chopped
2 Oxo vegetable cubes
600ml/1 pint hot water
Black pepper

Spray a saucepan with oil. Cook celery and onion, covered, approximately 5 minutes, stirring occasionally. Dissolve stock cubes in the hot water and add to the pan.

Simmer until vegetables are tender. Allow to cool slightly and liquidise. Re-heat as necessary and season with black pepper.

Carrot & Coriander Soup

Serves

INGREDIENTS

1 small onion, chopped
1 clove garlic, crushed
350g/12 oz carrots, sliced
900ml/1½ pints chicken or vegetable stock
2 tbsp chopped fresh or frozen coriander
Sprigs of coriander to garnisha

Place all ingredients into a saucepan. Bring to the boil, reduce heat, cover and simmer 20 minutes.

Cool slightly then liquidise.

Serve garnished with a small sprig of coriander.

Muligatawny Soup

Serves

INGREDIENTS

200g/7 oz onions, sliced
200g/7 oz carrots, sliced
1 tbsp hot Madras curry powder (or to taste)
2 x 400g cans tomatoes
2 Bovril Beef cubes

Place carrots and onions into a saucepan with 150ml/¼ pint water. Bring to the boil, reduce heat, cover and simmer 10 minutes. Remove lid and stir in curry powder.

Add tomatoes, breaking them up, and crumble in stock cubes. Stir well, cover and simmer 15 minutes.

Allow to cool a little and either liquidise all the soup, or liquidise half the soup and mix with remaining half.

If too thick, stir in additional water and re-heat gently before serving.

No-Check
Curried Butternut Squash Soup

Serves 4

Courtesy of Class Assistant Jaqui McIntosh, Edinburgh

INGREDIENTS

1 medium butternut squash, peeled and cubed
2 medium onions, chopped
2 sticks celery, sliced
2 cloves garlic, crushed
1 tbsp curry powder, or to taste
1 Oxo chicken or vegetable cube

Place all ingredients in a large saucepan and cover with water. Bring to the boil, then cover and simmer until vegetables are soft, stirring now and again.

Allow to cool a little then liquidise until smooth, adding a little extra water if necessary.

Best if left a few hours for flavours to develop. Re-heat gently.

No-Check
Three Tomato Soup

Serves 4

INGREDIENTS

30g/1 oz dried sun-dried tomatoes
250g/9 oz fresh tomatoes
2 x 400g cans plum tomatoes
1 medium onion, chopped
1 clove garlic, crushed
Spray oil
150ml/¼ pint vegetable stock
2 tsp granulated sweetener
A few fresh basil leaves, finely shredded

Snip the sun-dried tomatoes into small pieces, cover with a little boiling water and leave to hydrate 10-15 minutes.

Pour boiling water over fresh tomatoes and leave 2-3 minutes. Remove carefully, peel, de-seed and chop roughly.

Soften onions and garlic in pan sprayed with oil. Add canned tomatoes, bring to a simmer and cook gently 10 minutes, stirring now and again. Allow to cool a little, then liquidise until smooth. Pass through a sieve to remove seeds and return to pan.

Stir in sun-dried tomatoes with liquid, fresh tomatoes, stock and sweetener. Heat gently and serve garnished with finely shredded basil.

Red Onion & Tomato Soup

Serves

Spray oil
250 g/9 oz red onions, peeled and sliced
2 medium carrots, peeled and sliced
400g can chopped tomatoes
½ tsp dried sage
600 ml/chicken or vegetable stock
½ tsp granulated sweetener
Black pepper

Spray a pan with oil and cook the red onions very gently until softened and coloured, about 20-30 minutes, stirring now and again.

Meanwhile, put the carrots, tomatoes, sage and stock into a large saucepan. Bring to a simmer and cook about 15-20 minutes until the carrots are tender.

Use a potato masher to crush the tomato and carrot mixture.

Add the sweetener and black pepper to taste.

Stir in the red onions and, if required, re-heat gently before serving.

Tasty Tomato Soup

Serves

Courtesy of class manager Diane Marlee

225g/8 oz carrots, chopped
225g/8 oz swede/turnip, chopped
1 medium onion, chopped
400g can of tomatoes
2 tbsp tomato purée
3 bay leaves
900ml/1½ pints vegetable stock
Granulated sweetener, to taste (optional)

Place chopped vegetables in a large saucepan together with tomatoes, tomato purée, bay leaves and vegetable stock.

Bring to the boil, cover and simmer until vegetables are tender.

Allow to cool slightly, remove bay leaves and liquidise. Add granulated sweetener to taste, 1 tsp at a time (optional).

Sweet & Sour Soup

Courtesy of member Agnes Latta, Bathgate

Serves 3 to 4

INGREDIENTS

400g can tomatoes, chopped
1 small onion, chopped
8 ready-to-eat dried apricots, chopped
½ tsp cumin
600ml/1 pint chicken or vegetable stock

Place all ingredients into a saucepan. Bring to the boil, then simmer gently 30 minutes.

Allow to cool a little then blend until smooth.

May be served hot or cold.

> * One-quarter of the recipe uses half of one average serving Every Day Bonus fruit.
>
> If not using Every Day Bonus fruit, count 1 Check per one-quarter of the recipe.

Curried Cauliflower & Carrot Soup

Serves 4

INGREDIENTS

300 g/10 oz small cauliflower florets
300 g/10 oz carrots, peeled and sliced
1 medium onion, peeled and chopped
1 dspn curry powder
2 dspn tomato purée
3 Oxo vegetable cubes
900 ml/1½ pints hot water

Put the vegetables, curry powder and tomato purée into a large saucepan.

Dissolve the vegetable cubes in the hot water and add to the pan.

Bring to the boil, cover and simmer approximately 20 minutes or until vegetables are tender.

Either serve chunky, or crush with a potato masher.

Carrot & Chilli Soup

Serves 4

INGREDIENTS

450g/1lb carrots, sliced
175g/6 oz onions, chopped
1 medium red chilli, de-seeded and sliced
900ml/1½ pints chicken or vegetable stock
Lime wedges (optional)

Put carrots, onions, chilli and stock into a large saucepan. Bring to the boil, then cover and simmer about 15 minutes, or until carrots are tender.

Allow to cool a little, then blend until smooth.

Re-heat as necessary and, if liked, serve with a squeeze of lime juice.

Hungarian Red Cabbage Soup

Serves 4

INGREDIENTS

Spray oil
1 onion, finely chopped
1 garlic clove, crushed
375 g/12 oz red cabbage, shredded
½ tsp caraway seeds
400g can chopped tomatoes
900 ml/1½ pints vegetable stock
1 tsp red wine vinegar
Salt and black pepper
Chopped fresh dill, to garnish

Spray a large saucepan lightly with oil. Cook the onion, garlic and red cabbage over a low heat, stirring occasionally, until tender.

Add the caraway seeds, tomatoes, stock and vinegar. Season with salt and pepper and bring to the boil.

Reduce the heat to a simmer, cover with a lid and cook gently for 30 minutes.

Serve sprinkled with a little dill.

variation:

This soup is even more delicious if you top each bowl with a rounded tbsp of virtually fat-free fromage frais. This is about one-quarter of Every Day Bonus milk/yoghurt allowance. If not using Every Day Bonus allowance, count 1 Check 0g fat per serving.

No-Check *using Every Day Bonus milk**

Bortch

Serves **4**

INGREDIENTS

600ml/1 pint beef stock
250g pack cooked and peeled beetroot (no vinegar), roughly chopped
1 medium onion, chopped
115g/4 oz savoy cabbage, shredded
300-450ml/½-¾ pint warm water
Black pepper
1 rounded tbsp low-fat natural yoghurt per serving

Put stock into a large saucepan and bring to the boil.

Add beetroot and onion, cover and simmer 10 minutes. Add cabbage and cook covered a further 10 minutes.

Allow to cool a little, then transfer to a liquidiser and blend gradually adding about 300-450ml/½-¾ pint extra warm water, until smooth and velvety.

Re-heat gently and season with black pepper.

Swirl 1 rounded tbsp low-fat natural yoghurt into each serving.

* 1 rounded tbsp low-fat natural yoghurt is the equivalent of one-quarter of Every Day Bonus milk/yoghurt allowance.

If not using Every Day Bonus allowance, count 1 Check per 1 rounded tbsp low-fat natural yoghurt.

Leek & 'Neep Soup

Serves **4**

INGREDIENTS

- 300g/10 oz washed and sliced leeks
- 300g/10 oz white turnip, chopped
- 2 cloves garlic, crushed
- 900ml/1½ pints vegetable stock
- Black pepper

Place all ingredients into a large saucepan. Bring to the boil, cover, reduce heat and simmer until vegetables are tender, stirring occasionally.

Turn out heat and use a potato masher to crush vegetables. If too thick add extra water.

Re-heat as necessary and serve sprinkled with black pepper.

Cauliflower & Broccoli Soup

Serves **4**

INGREDIENTS

- 250g/9 oz fresh or frozen cauliflower florets
- 250g/9 oz fresh or frozen broccoli florets
- 1 onion, peeled and chopped
- 900ml/1½ pints chicken or vegetable stock
- Freshly grated nutmeg to garnish

Place all ingredients, except nutmeg, into a saucepan. Bring to the boil, cover, reduce heat and simmer 20 minutes.

Allow to cool slightly, then liquidise. Serve with a grating of nutmeg.

No-Check
Starters

No-Check
Stuffed Red Pepper

Serves to

INGREDIENTS

1 red pepper
2-3 button mushrooms, sliced
1 small tomato, skinned and quartered
1 clove garlic, peeled and chopped
Salt & black pepper
Spray oil

Pre-heat oven to 190°C/gas mark 5.

Halve pepper through the stalk and remove seeds, leaving stalk intact.

Fill pepper halves with mushroom slices and tomato. Sprinkle with chopped garlic, season lightly with salt and black pepper and spray lightly with oil.

Bake approximately 45 minutes, or until pepper is cooked and "charred" around the edges.

Serve as a starter, or as an accompaniment to rice or pasta dishes, or simply as a delicious snack.

Mighty Mushrooms

INGREDIENTS

45g/1½ oz frozen mixed peppers
2 button mushrooms, finely chopped
1 small clove garlic, finely chopped
1 small tomato, chopped
Small pinch dried oregano or thyme
Salt and black pepper
2 large "saucer" (Portobello) mushrooms
Spray oil, preferably olive oil flavour

Pre-heat oven to 220°C/gas mark 8.

Allow peppers to defrost a little and cut into dice, if not already chopped. Put in a sieve and rinse under cold water to defrost completely. Drain on kitchen paper.

Mix peppers with chopped mushrooms, garlic, tomato and herbs. Season to taste.

Spray white side of "saucer" mushrooms with oil, turn over and pile mixture on top. Place on a non-stick baking tray and bake approximately 15-20 minutes, until juices start to run.

Carrot & Thyme Mousse

Serves 4

INGREDIENTS

400g/14 oz peeled weight, carrots
200ml/⅓ pint vegetable stock
½ tsp fresh or frozen thyme
1 egg white

Pre-heat oven to 190°C/gas mark 5.

Cut carrots into chunks and place in a saucepan with stock. Bring to the boil, cover and simmer 15-20 minutes until tender.

Allow to cool a little and liquidise to a smooth, thick purée adding up to 3 tbsp water if necessary.

Whisk egg white until stiff and dry. Using a metal spoon, gradually fold purée into white.

Divide the mixture between 4 small 150ml/5 fl.oz ramekins and place in a roasting tin. Fill tin with water to come halfway up the sides of the ramekins.

Bake approximately 45 minutes or until top is firm to the touch. Serve warm as a starter.

Little Stuffed Mushrooms

Serves

INGREDIENTS

6 button or small chestnut mushrooms
6 thin slivers of garlic
Black pepper
6 basil leaves
6 cherry tomatoes
Spray oil

Pre-heat oven to 220°C/gas mark 8.

Remove the stalks from the mushrooms (and save for use in another recipe). Place the mushrooms on a baking tray, stalk-side uppermost.

Place a sliver of garlic in each mushroom and season with black pepper.

Place a basil leaf, then a cherry tomato in each mushroom. Pierce the tomatoes with the point of a sharp knife.

Spray lightly with oil and roast in the pre-heated oven approximately 15 minutes until the juices start to run.

Aubergine & Red Pepper Pâté

Serves 2 to 3

INGREDIENTS

1 aubergine, approximately 300-400g/10-14 oz
1 medium red pepper, approximately 150g/5 oz
2 cloves garlic
1 dspn finely chopped parsley
Salt and black pepper

tip:

Add 2 Checks to serve pâté on crispbread or 3 Checks to serve with 1 slice Melba Toast.

Pre-heat oven to 220°C/gas mark 8.

Remove stalks from aubergine and pepper and cut in half lengthways. De-seed pepper. Wrap garlic cloves in foil. Place aubergines and peppers cut-side down on a non-stick baking tray together with garlic. Bake approximately 30-35 minutes until aubergines start to collapse and pepper skins are blistered and charred.

Place peppers in a polythene bag 10 minutes to steam, then peel and dice flesh.

When cool enough to handle, place aubergines in a sieve over a bowl and press out bitter juices with a spoon. Scoop aubergine flesh away from skin into a blender. Squeeze in garlic cloves releasing softened flesh. Blend in a few short bursts, mixing with a fork in between. Consistency should be fairly smooth.

Transfer aubergine to a bowl and stir in diced peppers, chopped parsley and seasoning to taste. Serve at room temperature.

Above quantity is enough for 2 good servings as a starter. If doubling quantities for 4, oven time may be a bit longer.

Tomato & Basil Sorbet

Serves 2

INGREDIENTS

6 fresh ripe tomatoes
Kettle of boiling water
5 g/¼ oz basil leaves
1 tsp granulated sweetener
1 tsp tomato purée
2 sprigs of small basil leaves to garnish

tip:
This dish is a great 'starter' course, eaten before one of our Low Check Pasta main courses

With a sharp pointed knife, slash a cross in the skin at the base of each tomato.

Pour the boiling water into a bowl or jug. Place 3 of the tomatoes in the boiling water and leave for 1 minute. Remove carefully with a spoon and they should be easy to peel, starting at the cross. Replace the water with fresh boiling water and repeat with remaining tomatoes.

Cut the tomatoes in half and remove the seeds, then cut each half in two removing any green stalk. Place the tomatoes on a tray or plate and place in the freezer about 1-1½ hours until icy and firm but not frozen solid. (If you have to leave them longer and they go rock solid, you can microwave them for about 2 minutes on defrost.)

When ready to serve, shred the basil finely. Remove the tomatoes from the freezer and place half in a liquidiser together with half the basil, half the sweetener and half the tomato purée.

Blitz in short bursts, stopping to push the mixture down from the sides of the liquidiser with a spatula and breaking up the tomatoes, until you have a fairly smooth consistency.

Spoon the mixture into a ramekin then repeat the process with the other half of the tomatoes and ingredients.

Serve immediately, garnished with sprigs of small basil leaves.

Beany Bundles

Serves 2

INGREDIENTS

- ½ large red pepper (cut from stalk to base)
- 150-175 g/5-6 oz whole fine green beans (haricots verts)
- 2 rounded tbsp virtually fat-free natural yoghurt
- 1 dspn lemon juice
- 1 tsp chopped fresh parsley
- 1 tsp chopped fresh mint or thyme
- A little freshly grated lemon zest
- Salt and pepper

Grill the cut side of the pepper until starting to soften. Turn over and grill the skin side until charred. Allow to cool. Remove skin, then cut the pepper into 6-8 long thin strips.

Steam or microwave the beans until just tender. Allow to cool.

Take about 5 beans at a time and wrap a strip of pepper around their middle (as if tying them into bundles). Lay 3 or 4 bundles on each plate.

Mix together the yoghurt, lemon juice and herbs. Grate a little lemon zest into the dressing and stir in. If required, season to taste.

Beans are best eaten at room temperature rather than straight from the fridge. Use a spoon to drizzle the dressing over the beans just before serving.

No-Check

Courgettes Provençale

Serves

INGREDIENTS

1 onion, finely chopped
1-2 cloves garlic, crushed
Spray oil
400g can chopped tomatoes
1 tsp red wine vinegar
½ tsp Herbes de Provence
4 medium courgettes, sliced thickly
Salt and black pepper

Place onions and garlic in a medium saucepan sprayed with oil. Cover and cook gently until soft, stirring frequently.

Add tomatoes, red wine vinegar and herbs. Bring to the boil and stir in courgettes. Cover and simmer gently approximately 15 minutes, or until courgettes are tender. Season to taste (may not be necessary).

Serve either hot or cold (at room temperature).

No-Check

Ratatouille Towers

Serves 2

INGREDIENTS

Spray oil
1 small aubergine, sliced
1 medium courgette, sliced diagonally
1 garlic clove, crushed
200 g/7 oz canned chopped tomatoes
Dash of balsamic vinegar (optional)
Salt and pepper

variation:

If wished, you can sprinkle the top of each tower before cooking with 1 level tsp grated parmesan cheese, which will add 0.5 Check 1g fat per serving.

Lightly spray a griddle pan with oil and, when hot, cook the sliced aubergine and courgettes in batches until lightly golden brown and attractively striped on both sides. Remove from the pan.

Spray a small saucepan with a little oil and cook the garlic and tomatoes until reduced and thickened. Add the balsamic vinegar and season to taste.

Take 2 individual ovenproof dishes and place an aubergine slice in the base of each one. Spoon in a little tomato sauce and cover with a courgette slice. Continue layering up in this way until all the vegetables and sauce are used.

Bake in a pre-heated oven 200°C/gas mark 6 for 15 minutes.

Turn out the towers and serve with a crisp salad.

No-Check Meals

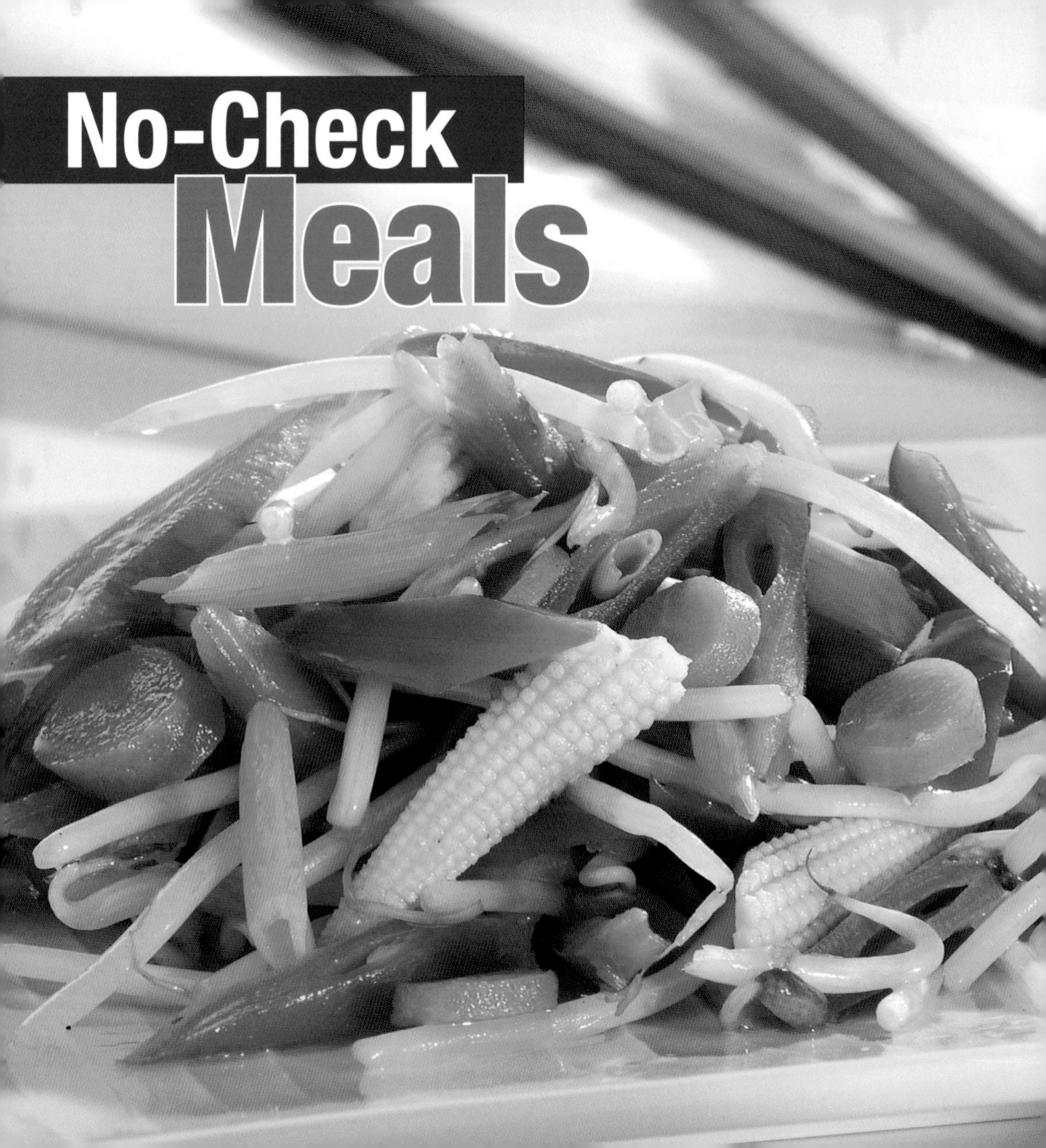

Super Stir Fry

Serves 1

INGREDIENTS

Spray oil
½ red pepper, sliced, or a good handful of frozen mixed peppers
1 carrot, cut into thin strips or slices
3-4 spring onions, sliced diagonally
1 clove garlic, crushed
Handful of fresh or frozen mangetout or green beans
115g/4 oz fresh beansprouts or shredded savoy cabbage
A few fresh, frozen or canned baby sweetcorn
1 Chinese Oxo cube
1-2 tbsp water

Spray pan with oil and cook peppers and carrots 3-4 minutes, stirring frequently.

Add spring onions and garlic and stir-fry 1 minute.

Stir in mangetout and beansprouts (or alternatives), baby sweetcorn and crumbled Chinese cube. Add water and stir-fry approximately 2 minutes.

Serve on it's own as a "free lunch", or serve a portion with cooked chicken, pork chops or salmon fillets (counting Checks as appropriate).

nb:
The above is a general guide.
You can experiment with any other
vegetables you have to hand.

Mushroom Stroganoff

Serves

INGREDIENTS

- 1 small onion, chopped
- Spray oil
- 115g/4 oz mushrooms, roughly chopped
- 1 Oxo vegetable cube
- 1 dspn tomato purée
- Pinch of thyme
- 100g/2 heaped tbsp fat-free natural fromage frais
- Black pepper
- 1 dspn chopped fresh parsley

Cook onions gently in pan sprayed with oil until softened and starting to brown. Add 1-2 tbsp water, if necessary, to prevent sticking.

Add mushrooms, crumbled vegetable cube, tomato purée and thyme. Stir 1 minute. Add 100ml/3½ fl.oz hot water and simmer gently 3-4 minutes.

Remove pan from heat and stir in fromage frais. Return to heat and warm gently stirring for a few seconds. Sprinkle with black pepper and chopped parsley.

Either serve on it's own or add a portion of rice or mashed potatoes for a more substantial meal (counting Checks as appropriate).

* Fromage frais used in recipe is the equivalent of half of Every Day Bonus milk/yoghurt allowance.

If not using Every Day Bonus allowance, count 2 Checks for the whole recipe.

Vegetable Chilli

Serves 1 to 2

INGREDIENTS

1 onion, sliced
Spray oil
1 clove garlic, crushed
150g/5 oz frozen sliced mixed peppers
1 tsp chilli powder, or to taste
Good pinch cumin
400g can tomatoes
½ Oxo vegetable cube
1 courgette, sliced
3 mushrooms, roughly chopped

Soften onion in pan sprayed with oil. Add garlic, peppers and spices and stir-fry 2-3 minutes.

Stir in tomatoes, crumbled vegetable cube, courgettes and mushrooms. Bring to a simmer, cover and cook gently 15-20 minutes, stirring occasionally.

variation:

For a more substantial meal, rinsed and drained canned kidney beans can be added with the courgettes and mushrooms.

Count 1 Check per rounded tbsp kidney beans.

No-Check

Vegetable Bolognese

No need for pasta with this hearty dish!

Serves 2 to 3

Courtesy of member Louise Goodchild, Margate

INGREDIENTS

2 large carrots
1 large onion, chopped
5-6 mushrooms, roughly chopped
1 medium courgette, sliced or chopped
150g/5 oz white cabbage, finely shredded
400g can tomatoes
1 clove garlic, crushed
½ tsp mixed herbs
Salt and pepper

Peel carrots. Grate one and cut the other into matchsticks or small dice.

Place all ingredients into a large saucepan. Bring to the boil, stirring continuously and breaking up the tomatoes.

Cover and simmer gently 20-30 minutes, stirring occasionally, until vegetables are tender. Season to taste.

Serve on it's own as a "free lunch", or serve a portion with cooked chicken or prawns or a small portion of pasta (counting Checks as appropriate).

Simple Vegetable Korma

Serves

INGREDIENTS

1 small onion, chopped
Spray oil
1 clove garlic, crushed
1 dspn korma curry powder, or other mild curry powder
115g/4 oz cauliflower florets
115g/4 oz carrots, peeled and sliced
150ml/¼ pint chicken or vegetable stock
115g/4 oz frozen sliced green beans
2 heaped tbsp diet natural yoghurt or 0% fat Greek yoghurt

Cook onion gently in a medium saucepan sprayed with oil until soft and starting to colour. Add garlic and curry powder and stir over gentle heat 1 minute.

Add cauliflower, carrots and stock. Bring to a simmer, cover and cook 20 minutes, stirring occasionally. Add green beans, return to a simmer, cover and cook 5 minutes more.

Remove from heat, leave for 1 minute then tilt pan and stir yoghurt well into juices. Mix sauce through vegetables.

> ** Yoghurt used in recipe is the equivalent of half of Every Day Bonus milk/yoghurt allowance.*
>
> *If not using Every Day Bonus allowance, count 2 Checks for the whole recipe.*

No-Check *side dish*

Spiced Onions

Serves ❶

INGREDIENTS

1 small onion, chopped
2 dspn tomato ketchup
2 dspn tomato purée
1 tsp dried mint
Pinch of chilli powder
Pinch of salt

Mix all the ingredients well and serve as a dip or side dish.

Leafy Lasagne

Serves 2

INGREDIENTS

Spray oil
1 onion, chopped
1 garlic clove, crushed
1 tbsp tomato purée
400g can chopped tomatoes
Good pinch Italian seasoning
1 Oxo chicken or vegetable cube
1 small aubergine, cut into cubes
1 large courgette, sliced
1 large carrot, sliced
6 large savoy cabbage leaves
200g pot virtually fat-free natural fromage frais
Salt and black pepper
A little grated nutmeg

variation:

Before placing under the grill, sprinkle the fromage frais with 2 level dspn grated parmesan cheese, which will give a golden colour after heating. Add 1 Check 2g fat per serving.

Spray a saucepan with oil and heat. Cook the onion and garlic gently until softened. Stir in the tomato purée and cook 1 minute, stirring.

Add the chopped tomatoes, Italian seasoning, crumble in the stock cube and stir together well. Stir in the aubergine, courgettes, and carrots. Bring to a simmer, cover and cook gently about 20 minutes, stirring occasionally.

Remove the tough stalks from the cabbage leaves and cook in boiling water about 2 minutes until starting to soften. Drain well.

Place 2 cabbage leaves in the bottom of a shallow heatproof dish. Top with half the vegetable mixture. Repeat layers and finish with a layer of cabbage leaves.

Season the fromage frais with a tiny pinch of salt and lots of black pepper. Spread over cabbage leaves and sprinkle with a little grated nutmeg.

Cook lasagne 5-10 minutes under a pre-heated hot grill, until fromage frais is firm. Serve half the recipe to each person.

* Half this recipe (1 serving) uses the equivalent of half Every Day Bonus milk/yoghurt allowance. If not using this allowance, count 2 Checks 0g fat per serving.

Stuffed Aubergine

Serves

1 medium aubergine
1 onion, chopped
1 medium carrot, diced,
1 medium stick celery, finely sliced
1 tbsp tomato purée
Pinch of mixed herbs
Salt and pepper

variation:

After filling with vegetable mixture, on each half, sprinkle over 1 tbsp fresh wholemeal breadcrumbs and 1 tsp grated parmesan cheese. Bake until crumbs are golden, about 15-20 minutes. Count 2 Checks for the whole recipe.

Pre-heat oven to 200°C/gas mark 6.

Cut aubergine in half lengthways. Scoop out and retain centres, leaving 2 "shells". Sprinkle inside of shells lightly with salt and place cut-side down on a baking tray. Bake 20 minutes.

Meanwhile, plunge onion, carrot, celery and chopped flesh removed from centre of aubergine into boiling water, then cover and cook at a gentle boil approximately 15 minutes until softened. Drain vegetables, roughly mash with a fork and stir in tomato purée and herbs. If necessary, season lightly with salt and pepper (celery and tomato purée add a lot of flavour, often making it unnecessary to add salt).

Remove shells from oven, turn over and fill with vegetable mixture. Return to oven 15 minutes, until aubergine is soft.

No-Check
Egg-White Omelette

Serves 1

INGREDIENTS

3 button mushrooms, sliced
1 tomato, chopped
Spray oil
2 medium egg whites
Pinch of salt
Spray oil

Cook mushrooms and tomatoes in a non-stick pan sprayed with oil. Remove from pan and keep warm.

Beat egg whites until just foamy. Season with pinch of salt.

Re-spray pan. Pour egg whites over base of pan and cook very gently until just set. Ease a spatula under the edges of the omelette to prevent sticking.

Place cooked filling on one side of omelette and fold over other side.

No-Check
Vegetable Goulash

Serves 2

INGREDIENTS

1 medium onion, sliced
1 clove garlic, crushed
2 sticks celery or 1 small leek, sliced
2 large carrots, sliced
1 green, or other colour, pepper, de-seeded and sliced
4 tomatoes, roughly chopped
1 tbsp paprika
2 tbsp water
Salt and pepper

Cook onions and garlic in a large non-stick saucepan until softened. Adding a little water and covering with a lid helps speed up the process, but check and stir frequently.

Add celery or leeks, carrots and peppers. Cover and cook 10 minutes over moderate heat, stirring now and again.

Stir in tomatoes, paprika, water and seasoning. Cover and simmer gently approximately 20 minutes or until vegetables are just tender.

Serve on it's own as a "free lunch" , or serve a portion with cooked pork or beef (counting Checks as appropriate).

nb:

Using just 1 Check 0g fat, you can top each portion with 1 rounded tbsp of fat-free natural yoghurt before serving.

No-Check
Vegetable Curry

Serves **2** *to* **4**

INGREDIENTS

Spray oil

2 medium onions, sliced

1 garlic clove, crushed

2 dspn curry powder

1 tsp turmeric

1 Oxo vegetable cube

400 ml/⅔ pint hot water

1 tbsp tomato purée

1 tbsp lemon juice

450 g/1 lb cauliflower or mixture
   of cauliflower and broccoli

2 medium carrots, sliced

250 g/9 oz frozen sliced green beans

1-2 tomatoes, chopped

Salt

Spray a large non-stick saucepan with oil. Spread the onions and garlic over the base of the pan, cover and cook very gently 15 minutes until soft and starting to brown.

Sprinkle in the curry powder and turmeric. Cover and cook over very low heat 2 minutes to release spice flavours.

Dissolve stock cube in hot water and stir into pan together with tomato purée, lemon juice, cauliflower and carrots. Cover and simmer gently 30-45 minutes, stirring occasionally.

Add green beans and tomatoes, cover and simmer 10-15 minutes. Season to taste.

Turnip Rosti 5-a-day Pie

Serves

INGREDIENTS

150 g/5 oz small whole white turnip
115 g/4 oz leek, cut into chunks
1 large carrot, sliced
4-5 small fresh or frozen broccoli florets
1 stick celery, sliced
½ Oxo vegetable cube
Pinch of mixed herbs
Black pepper
Spray oil

Cook all the vegetables, except the turnip, in boiling water until just tender.

Peel the turnip and cook whole 5 minutes in boiling water. Drain and, when cool enough to handle, grate it coarsely.

Drain the vegetables reserving 100 ml/3½ fl oz of the cooking liquid. Dissolve the Oxo cube in the reserved liquid.

Pack the vegetables and stock into a heatproof dish and scatter the grated turnip over the top. Sprinkle with herbs and black pepper and spray lightly with oil.

Brown about 10 minutes under a pre-heated hot grill.

variation:

Chop 2 wafer-thin slices ham and mix with the vegetables before topping with the grated turnip. Add 1 Check 1g fat for the whole recipe.

note:

The total weight of vegetables in this recipe is at least 400g/14 oz – the amount equal to "5-a-day" portions of fruit and veg!

Salads

Indian Fruit & Radish Salad

Serves

INGREDIENTS

60 g/2 oz mango flesh
2 spring onions, shredded
½ red pepper, deseeded and sliced into shreds
4-6 large radishes, thinly sliced
1 tbsp oil-free dressing
Grated zest and juice of 1 lime
Pinch of chilli powder
1 tsp grated fresh root ginger
Few fresh coriander leaves, shredded

Cut the mango flesh into matchstick strips. Mix in a bowl with the spring onions, red pepper and radishes.

Blend the oil-free dressing with the lime zest and juice, chilli powder and grated ginger.

Toss the salad gently in the dressing and serve sprinkled with fresh coriander.

* The mango in this recipe uses about one-quarter of Every Day Bonus fruit allowance. If not using fruit from this allowance, count 1 Check 0g fat for the whole recipe.

Greens & Citrus Salad

Serves **1**

INGREDIENTS

30g/1 oz prepared mixed dark salad leaves, including baby spinach leaves and/or watercress
1 satsuma or tangerine
1 small trimmed spring onion
Lemon juice
Black pepper

Arrange salad leaves on serving plate or side-salad bowl. Peel and segment the satsuma or tangerine and arrange on salad leaves.

Finely slice the spring onion and scatter over salad. Sprinkle with plenty of lemon juice and season with black pepper.

Good served as a side dish with spicy foods.

> ** Whole recipe uses half of one average serving Every Day Bonus fruit.*
>
> *If not using Every Day Bonus fruit, count 1 Check for the whole recipe.*

No-Check

Chinese Salad

Serves **1** *to* **2**

INGREDIENTS

225g can beansprouts
1 large carrot, coarsely grated
1 stick celery, finely sliced
2-3 spring onions, sliced
60g/2 oz red pepper, chopped
1 dspn light soy sauce
1 tsp wine vinegar
1 tsp granulated sweetener
Pinch Chinese 5-spice powder
1 tsp water

Drain the beansprouts. Mix all vegetables together.

Stir together soy sauce, wine vinegar, sweetener, 5-spice powder and water. Sprinkle over salad and mix in well.

nb:

> *If you wish to use fresh beansprouts, blanch around 150g/5 oz in boiling water for 1 minute. Drain and cool then proceed with recipe.*

No-Check
Artichoke Heart & Tomato Salad

Serves 2 to 4

INGREDIENTS

400g can artichoke hearts
12 baby plum tomatoes or cherry tomatoes
Balsamic vinegar

Drain artichoke hearts into a sieve and rinse well under cold running water. Cut into quarters.

Halve baby plum tomatoes and mix with artichokes.

Serve out required amount and sprinkle with a few drops balsamic vinegar.

No-Check
Marinated Mushrooms & Courgettes

Serves 2

INGREDIENTS

60g/2 oz button mushrooms, sliced
115g/4 oz courgettes, thinly sliced
2 tbsp oil-free Italian
   dressing/vinaigrette (e.g. Kraft Fat Free)

Mix mushroom and courgette slices together in a shallow dish. Spoon over dressing and mix in well. Cover, refrigerate and leave to marinate at least 1 hour, stirring occasionally.

Serve as a starter, or side salad to accompany pasta dishes.

No-Check

Green Bean & Cherry Tomato Salad

Serves 1 to 2

INGREDIENTS

175g/6 oz frozen sliced green beans
6 cherry tomatoes, halved
2 tsp balsamic vinegar
Salt and black pepper

Steam or microwave beans until just tender. Drain and cool. Mix beans with tomatoes, sprinkle with balsamic vinegar and season to taste.

No-Check

Coleslaw

Serves 2 to 4

INGREDIENTS

115g/4 oz white cabbage, finely shredded
115g/4 oz carrots, coarsely grated
3-4 tbsp Kraft Fat Free Italian Dressing

Simply mix all ingredients together.

No-Check

Carrot, Sushi Ginger & Lemon Salad

Serves 2 to 4

INGREDIENTS

2 large carrots, coarsely grated
1 tbsp sushi ginger (e.g. Blue Dragon)
1 tbsp lemon juice

Chop any large pieces of ginger. Mix together carrots and ginger. Sprinkle with lemon juice.

Roasted Four Pepper Salad

Serves

INGREDIENTS

- 1 red pepper
- 1 green pepper
- 1 orange pepper
- 1 yellow pepper
- A little rocket or pretty salad leaves for garnish
- Balsamic vinegar

Pre-heat oven to 220°C/gas mark 8.

Remove stalk and seeds from peppers and cut into quarters. Place skin-side-up on a large baking tray. Roast in the hottest part of the oven approximately 30-40 minutes, or until skins are blistered and charred.

Put peppers in a polythene bag 10 minutes to steam. Remove, peel and allow to cool.

For each serving, arrange 1 piece of each colour pepper on a serving plate, garnished with a few salad leaves. Sprinkle with a little balsamic vinegar.

Warm Spinach & Mushroom Salad

Serves

INGREDIENTS

- 1 red pepper
- 1 yellow pepper
- Spray oil
- 175 g/6 oz chestnut mushrooms, sliced or quartered
- 1 tsp balsamic vinegar
- 115 g/4 oz baby spinach leaves
- 1 tbsp oil-free dressing
- Salt and pepper
- Chopped fresh parsley

Put the peppers under a pre-heated hot grill and cook for a few minutes, turning them occasionally until the skins are blistered and charred.

Place in a plastic bag until cool, then peel off the skins, remove the seeds and cut into fine strips.

Spray a small pan lightly with oil and cook the mushrooms until golden-brown. Add the balsamic vinegar and cook for 1 minute.

Wash and dry the spinach and place in a bowl with the warm cooked peppers and mushrooms. Toss with the oil-free dressing and season to taste with salt and pepper. Scatter with parsley and serve.

Beetroot & Dill Salad

Serves 1

INGREDIENTS

150 g/5 oz cooked beetroot
2 spring onions, shredded
1 stick celery, shredded
Coarse sea salt
3 tbsp 0% fat Greek yoghurt or
  virtually fat-free fromage frais
½ tsp horseradish sauce
2-3 tbsp chopped fresh dill
Crisp lettuce leaves

Cut the cooked beetroot into thin sticks or batons. Mix in a bowl with the spring onions and celery and sprinkle with a little coarse sea salt.

Blend the yoghurt or fromage frais with the horseradish and dill until well combined.

Gently fold the beetroot mixture into the yoghurt mixture. Chill, if wished, before serving on a bed of crisp lettuce leaves.

> ** The yoghurt or fromage frais in this recipe is the equivalent of about half your Every Day Bonus milk/yoghurt allowance. If not using this allowance, count 2 Checks 0g fat for the whole recipe.*

Stuffed Cherry Tomato Salad

Serves 1

INGREDIENTS

5 ripe cherry tomatoes
5 tsp 0% fat Greek yoghurt
1 tbsp snipped chives
Salt and freshly ground black pepper
Small bag pre-washed
  rocket or watercress
2 tsp oil-free dressing
2 spring onions, finely sliced
Few fresh basil leaves

Cut each cherry tomato in half and scoop out the seeds.

Mix the Greek yoghurt with the chives and season to taste with salt and pepper.

Spoon the yoghurt mixture into the tomatoes.

Toss the rocket or watercress in the dressing and pile on to a plate. Scatter with the spring onions and basil leaves and arrange the stuffed cherry tomatoes on top.

> ** The yoghurt in this recipe is the equivalent of about one-quarter of Every Day Bonus milk/yoghurt allowance. If not using this allowance, count 1 Check 0g fat for the whole recipe.*

No-Check
Sides

Griddled Vegetable & Herb Platter

INGREDIENTS

Choose any of the following:

Sliced red, yellow and green peppers; sliced aubergine; courgette chunks; quartered red or white onions; chunks of celery; thickly sliced leeks; carrot batons; button mushrooms; cherry tomatoes

Spray oil

4 unpeeled whole garlic cloves

Sprigs of thyme, rosemary, oregano and sage

Sea salt crystals

Freshly ground black pepper

Prepare the vegetables of your choice, cutting them into slices, chunks or quarters.

Heat a cast iron griddle pan and spray lightly with oil. Add the prepared vegetables and tuck in the garlic cloves and herb sprigs.

Cook over a medium heat, turning frequently until the vegetables are tender and just slightly charred. Take care not to overcook them or they will turn into a burnt offering!

Remove from the heat and fish out the garlic. Squeeze the soft garlic out of the skins over the vegetables. Season with salt and pepper.

Remove any overcooked herb sprigs and replace with fresh ones, if wished, before serving.

No-Check

Griddled Courgettes

Slice courgettes lengthwise into long strips about ¼ cm/⅛ inch thick. Microwave on high 1 minute until just tender. Season lightly with salt. Spray a griddle pan with oil and heat. Cook courgettes about 5-7 minutes each side until tender and char-striped.

Roman-style Broccoli & Cauliflower

Serves 2 to 4

INGREDIENTS

1 head broccoli, divided into florets
1 small cauliflower, divided into florets
Spray olive oil
1 fresh red chilli, deseeded and finely chopped
2 garlic cloves, crushed
Salt and freshly ground black pepper
Squeeze of lemon juice

Cook the broccoli and cauliflower florets in a large pan of salted boiling water until just tender but still slightly firm. Drain well.

Spray a frying pan lightly with oil. When hot, add the chilli and garlic and toss quickly over a low heat.

Add the drained broccoli and cauliflower and cook for a few minutes, stirring occasionally.

Season with salt and pepper to taste. Add a squeeze of lemon juice and serve immediately.

variation:

For a more piquant flavour, you can drain 4 anchovy fillets in oil, rinse in water and pat dry. Mash with a wooden spoon and add to the pan with the garlic and chilli. This will add 1 Check 2g fat per serving for 2 people, or ½ Check 1g fat per serving for 4 people.

Mediterranean Vegetable Kebabs

Serves 4

INGREDIENTS

4 or 8 bamboo skewers
115g/4 oz courgette
85g/3 oz red onion
1 small red pepper
115g/4 oz aubergine
8 cherry tomatoes
Garlic powder
Salt and pepper
Spray oil

Soak the skewers in cold water 15 minutes to prevent scorching.

Cut all the vegetables, except the tomatoes, into 8 pieces. For 4 large kebabs, alternate 2 pieces of each vegetable and 2 cherry tomatoes on each skewer. For 8 smaller kebabs, thread 1 piece of each vegetable and 1 cherry tomato on each skewer.

Season with garlic powder, salt and pepper and spray lightly with oil. Grill under moderate heat, or barbecue, approximately 20-30 minutes until vegetables are tender and starting to char at the edges.

Leeks Provençale

Serves 4

INGREDIENTS

400g/14 oz trimmed weight, leeks
4 canned plum tomatoes
1 clove garlic, crushed
¼ tsp herbes de Provence
1 dspn red wine vinegar
1 tsp grated lemon zest
Salt and black pepper

Cut leeks in half lengthways, wash thoroughly and cut into 7cm/3 inch pieces. Cook leeks in a large pan, in about 2-3 cm/1 inch lightly salted boiling water for 3-4 minutes until just tender. Drain thoroughly and transfer to a serving dish.

Place a sieve over a medium saucepan. Over the sieve, remove seeds from tomatoes allowing juices to drain into the pan. Roughly chop the tomato flesh and add to pan together with crushed garlic and herbs. Bring to a simmer and cook 3-4 minutes. Stir in wine vinegar and lemon zest and season to taste. Cook 1-2 minutes more to reduce. Spread sauce over drained leeks, garnishing with a little extra grated lemon zest if you wish.

May be served either warm as an accompaniment, or cold, at room temperature, as a starter.

nb:

For a change, can also be made with lightly cooked mushrooms, marrow or courgettes instead of leeks.

Roasted Vegetables/Spread/Dip

Serves **4**

INGREDIENTS

2 red peppers, cut into large strips
2 onions, each cut into 6 wedges
2 medium courgettes, cut into chunks
1 small aubergine about 200g/7 oz, cut into 1cm/½ inch cubes
2-3 sprigs basil
1 unpeeled clove garlic
200ml/ ⅓ pint chicken or vegetable stock

Place vegetables into a large roasting dish. Add basil and garlic clove and pour stock over everything. Cover with foil.

If putting in the oven whilst, say, roasting a joint, cook for about 1 hour at 180°C/gas mark 4, until vegetables are softened, then remove foil and cook a further 20-30 minutes until vegetables are "roasted" and liquid almost absorbed.

If cooking alone, cook at 200°C/gas mark 6 for about 30 minutes before removing foil and cooking for a further 15-20 minutes.

Serve hot as an accompaniment or cold as a salad or starter.

For a spread or dip :

Remove garlic clove and roughly mash or blend some or all of the vegetables to a thick chunky spread/dip consistency. For a stronger taste, squeeze the softened garlic clove into the mixture. If too runny, stir in a teaspoon of tomato purée.

Use as a dip, or spread on hot toast or crispbreads or crackers (counting Checks as appropriate).

Peppered Swede Mash

Peel, chop and boil orange swede/turnip until soft. Or use half swede/turnip and half carrot.

Drain, reserving cooking liquid. Mash vegetables and use some of the cooking liquid if too stiff, or some skimmed milk from Every Day Bonus allowance.

Season with a little salt and plenty of coarsely ground black pepper.

variation:

Use pumpkin or butternut squash as an alternative to orange swede/turnip.

Cauliflower Mash

Boil cauliflower until soft. Mash lightly with a fork and season to taste. Can be used as a no-Check alternative to mashed potato or rice.

variation:

For Spiced Cauliflower Mash, make as above. Stir in some cumin, a tiny pinch at a time, according to taste, and serve sprinkled with a little garam masala. Use as an accompaniment to Middle Eastern dishes or curries.

Turnip & Parsley Mash

Peel, chop and boil white turnip until soft.

Drain, reserving cooking liquid. Mash using a little of the liquid or some skimmed milk from Every Day Bonus allowance.

Season to taste with salt and pepper and stir in some finely chopped parsley.

Celeriac & Lemon Mash

Peel and chop celeriac. Plunge into boiling water and boil until soft, about 10 minutes.

Drain, reserving cooking liquid. Mash, using a little of the liquid.

Stir in finely grated lemon zest, using about 1 tsp per 250-300g/9-10 oz peeled weight.

Season to taste with salt, pepper and a good squeeze of lemon juice.

Roasted Roots

Serves 4

INGREDIENTS

2 medium red or white onions, cut into wedges
2 medium carrots, cut into chunks
225g/8 oz white turnip, cut into 1cm/ ½ inch cubes
225g/8 oz orange turnip/swede, cut into 1 cm/½ inch cubes
2 sticks celery, thickly sliced
2 cloves garlic, halved
2-3 sprigs fresh rosemary or thyme or ½ tsp dried
300ml/½ pint chicken or vegetable stock
Black pepper

Pre-heat oven to 220°C/gas mark 8.

Place all vegetables in a large roasting dish. Add herbs and pour over stock. Cover tightly with foil and bake 45-60 minutes until vegetables are softened. (Extend cooking time if cooking at a lower temperature alongside other foods.)

Remove foil, stir vegetables and continue to cook uncovered 20 to 30 minutes or until roasted at the edges. Remove garlic cloves if preferred and season well with black pepper.

Carrot & Courgette Noodles

Use a vegetable peeler to cut long thin strips of courgette and carrot.

Place in boiling water and cook about 1 minute until just tender.

Drain and either serve hot as a vegetable accompaniment, or allow to cool and serve as a salad dressed with oil-free vinaigrette.

Leek & Green Bean Noodles

Use approximately equal amounts of leeks and green beans.

Thoroughly clean leek(s) by cutting through the centre lengthways and washing under running water. Cut into narrow strips.

Cook frozen sliced green beans in boiling water approximately 3 minutes. Add leek strips and cook a further 2 minutes.

Drain and either serve as a vegetable accompaniment, or top with low-fat pasta sauce (counting Checks in sauce as appropriate), or your own no-Check sauce made from onions, tomatoes and herbs.

No-Check
Sauces, Dressings & Chutneys

No-Check

Cucumber, Tomato & Onion Salsa

Serves 2 to 4

INGREDIENTS

5cm/2" cucumber
2 tomatoes
1-2 spring onions
Salt and black pepper
1 tbsp lemon juice
½ tsp Worcester sauce
½ tsp granulated sweetener

Cut the cucumber and tomatoes into small dice. Slice the spring onions. Mix all in a bowl together with any juices. Season to taste.

Mix together the lemon juice, Worcester sauce and sweetener and stir well into vegetables. Best if covered and left to marinate 30 minutes before serving, stirring once or twice.

No-Check *using Every Day Bonus milk**

Garlic & Herb Dressing/Dip

INGREDIENTS

100g fat-free fromage frais
2 good pinches garlic powder, or to taste
Good pinch of salt
¼ tsp granulated sweetener
1 dspn finely chopped fresh parsley

Stir the garlic powder, salt and sweetener into the fromage frais and mix well. Stir in the chopped parsley.

*The whole recipe is equivalent to half your Every Day Bonus milk allowance.

If not using Every Day Bonus milk, count 2 Checks for the whole recipe.

Spiced Carrot Dip

Serves 1 to 2

INGREDIENTS

2 large carrots, peeled and sliced
1 garlic clove, crushed
Juice of ½ lemon
Pinch of ground cumin
Pinch of cayenne pepper
2 tbsp 0% fat Greek yoghurt
Salt and freshly ground black pepper
Paprika for dusting
Raw vegetables to serve, e.g. celery, cucumber, broccoli florets, button mushrooms, strips of red, yellow and green peppers

Cook the prepared carrots in a pan of salted boiling water until tender. Drain and cool.

Spoon the cooked carrots into a blender or food processor, and add the garlic, lemon juice, ground cumin, cayenne and Greek yoghurt. Whizz for a few seconds until well blended and smooth.

Season to taste with salt and pepper and pour into a small dish. Dust with paprika, and serve with a selection of raw No-Check vegetables.

* The whole recipe uses the equivalent of about one-quarter Every Day Bonus milk/yoghurt allowance. If not using this allowance, count 1 Check 0g fat for the whole recipe.

No-Check

Cucumber, Celery & Mint Salsa

Serves 6 to 8

INGREDIENTS

½ cucumber
1 large stick of celery
4 spring onions, trimmed
2 tbsp chopped fresh mint leaves
Juice from ½ small lemon
Salt and pepper

Cut the cucumber in half lengthwise, remove the seeds and cut into small dice. Finely slice the celery and spring onions and mix with the cucumber.

Add the mint and lemon juice. Mix well and season to taste.

Good as an accompaniment to curries and spicy dishes (counting Checks as appropriate).

Red Onion & Balsamic Vinegar Chutney

Makes 8

INGREDIENTS

300-350 g/10-12 oz red onions
4 tbsp balsamic vinegar
150 ml/¼ pint water
1 tsp balsamic vinegar
2 dspn granulated sweetener, or to taste
Salt

Peel and thinly slice the onions and place in a saucepan together with 4 tbsp balsamic vinegar and the water.

Bring to the boil, turn heat down very low, cover the pan and gently cook the onions about 45-60 minutes, stirring now and again.

When onions are soft and almost all the liquid has evaporated, stir in 1 tsp balsamic vinegar, granulated sweetener to taste, and a little salt.

Turn up the heat and bring to the boil, stirring continuously for 1-2 minutes until the juices reduce and thicken.

Allow to cool and store in a covered container in the fridge (up to 10 days).

Use as an accompaniment to grilled or roast meats or with crackers and low-fat cheese or low-fat pâté (counting Checks as appropriate).

Oil-free Dressing

INGREDIENTS

½ tsp French mustard
½ tsp granulated sweetener
1 dspn white or light malt vinegar
1 dspn water
Salt and pepper

Mix together the mustard and sweetener. Stir in the vinegar and mix well. Add the water and season to taste.

Curry Sauce

INGREDIENTS

Spray oil
1 large onion, chopped
1 clove garlic, chopped
1 tbsp curry powder
1 tsp chilli powder
700g/1½ lb swede/orange turnip, chopped
900ml/1½ pints chicken or vegetable stock

nb:

A portion of the sauce may also be thinned with a little water, re-heated gently and served as a soup.

Spray a large saucepan with oil and cook onions until soft and starting to colour, adding a little water if necessary to prevent sticking. Add garlic and cook 1 minute. Stir in curry and chilli powders and cook about 30 seconds.

Add swede and stock, bring to the boil, cover and simmer until swede is tender. Allow to cool slightly and liquidise until smooth.

Re-heat as necessary and use with cooked meat, poultry, fish, prawns, vegetables or hard-boiled eggs (counting Checks as appropriate).

Mixed Pepper Salsa

Serves 4 to 6

INGREDIENTS

½ red pepper
½ green pepper
½ yellow or orange pepper
3-4 spring onions, trimmed
2 tbsp chopped parsley or coriander
2 tbsp fresh lime juice
Pinch of granulated sweetener
Good pinch chilli powder
Salt

Remove any seeds from the peppers and cut into small dice. Slice the spring onions and mix with the peppers together with the parsley or coriander.

Mix together the lime juice and sweetener. Stir in chilli powder and salt to taste. Stir into the pepper mixture. If possible, leave 30 minutes before serving to allow flavours to develop.

Good as an accompaniment to grilled or barbecued meats or poultry (counting Checks as appropriate).

Aubergine "Caviar"

Serves

INGREDIENTS

- 250 g/9 oz aubergine
- 2 large garlic cloves, unpeeled
- Fresh lemon juice
- 1 rounded tbsp virtually fat-free natural fromage frais
- Salt and pepper
- Selection of raw vegetable strips for dipping   (e.g. button mushrooms, strips of pepper, etc.)

* The fromage frais used in this recipe is equivalent to one-quarter of Every Day Bonus milk/yoghurt allowance. If not using this allowance, count ½ Check 0g fat per serving.

Pre-heat oven to 210°C/gas mark 7.

Cut the aubergine in half lengthwise and place cut-side down on a baking tray.

Bake in the pre-heated oven 15 minutes. Add the garlic cloves to the tray and cook approximately 10 minutes more until the aubergine is very soft. Remove from the oven and allow to cool.

Use a fork to scrape all the aubergine flesh away from the skin into a small bowl. Mash thoroughly with a fork. Gently squeeze the garlic cloves releasing the soft centres into the aubergine and mix well.

Stir in a good squeeze of fresh lemon juice and the fromage frais.

Season to taste with salt and pepper and serve with raw vegetables for dipping.

No-Check

Sweet & Sour Sauce or Dip

Courtesy of member Sonia Blackley, Portobello

INGREDIENTS

- 3 tbsp vinegar, preferably white
- 3 tbsp granulated sweetener
- 1 tbsp tomato purée
- 1 tbsp light or dark soy sauce
- Garlic powder or granules, to taste

Mix all ingredients together and microwave on high approximately 45 seconds to 1 minute. Add to stir-fries or use as a dipping sauce with vegetable sticks, grilled fish fingers, prawns, cooked chicken or duck or almost anything! (Count Checks as appropriate.)

Savoury Jellies/Chutneys

INGREDIENTS

**Approximately 200-250g/7-9 oz prepared No-Check vegetables
1 sachet sugar-free jelly
50-75ml/3-5 tbsp vinegar ****

Place prepared vegetables into a bowl or mould.

Put jelly crystals into a measuring jug and add boiling water up to the 450ml/¾ pint mark. Stir well to dissolve crystals. Stir in vinegar. Pour jelly over vegetables and mix well. Allow to cool, then chill in fridge until set.

Either unmould the jelly and serve in slices with cold meats and salad, (counting Checks as appropriate) or, take out required quantity and roughly chop to serve as a chutney.

Use:

grated carrot with orange or lemon jelly,

diced pickled, or cooked fresh, beetroot with blackcurrant jelly,

diced cucumber and chopped mint with lemon or lime jelly.

** Ideally use white or light malt vinegar (e.g. Sarson's) with light coloured jellies. Adjust the quantity you use according to personal taste, the sharpness of the jelly (e.g. lemon) and whether or not the vegetables were fresh or previously pickled (e.g. beetroot).

Rhubarb Jam

Courtesy of member Frances Thornton, Whitburn

2-3 sticks rhubarb
1 sachet sugar-free jelly crystals

Cut rhubarb into chunks and cook with 1-2 tbsp water until tender either on the hob or in the microwave. Immediately stir in jelly crystals thoroughly. Allow to cool and set. Store covered in the fridge for up to 2 weeks.

The mixture looks very firm when set, but spreads easily on toast, or add a good dollop to yoghurt, rice pudding or custard (counting Checks as appropriate).

nb:

One-third of a can of Hartley's No-Added-Sugar Solid Pack Rhubarb can be used instead of fresh rhubarb.

No-Check *using Every Day Bonus fruit**

Strawberry Chutney

150g/5 oz strawberries
1 tbsp balsamic vinegar
1½ tbsp water
½ tsp black pepper

Slice washed and hulled strawberries and place in a saucepan with remaining ingredients.

Cook uncovered over low heat approximately 25 minutes, stirring occasionally, until thickened.

Transfer to a covered container, cool and refrigerate.

* The whole recipe uses one average serving Every Day Bonus fruit.

If not using Every Day Bonus fruit, count 2 Checks for the whole recipe. Or for practical purposes, count half a Check for a serving of about one-sixth to one-quarter of the recipe.

No-Check
Desserts

Yoghurt Jelly

Serves 4

INGREDIENTS

300 ml/½ pint boiling water
1 sachet sugar-free jelly crystals, any flavour
2 x 125g pots virturally
   fat-free yoghurt, any flavour

Pour the boiling water into a jug or bowl, sprinkle over the jelly crystals stirring until completely dissolved. Allow to cool completely, but not set.

When the jelly is cold, whisk the yoghurt into the jelly (if the jelly is warm, the yoghurt will probably curdle). If preferred, pour into 4 individual serving dishes. Put in the fridge to set.

* This recipe uses the equivalent of approximately one-quarter of Every Day Bonus milk/yoghurt allowance per serving. If not using this allowance, count 1 Check 0g fat per serving.

No-Check

Strawberry & Appleade Jelly

Serves 4

INGREDIENTS

250 ml/ scant ½ pint boiling water
1 sachet strawberry flavour
   sugar-free jelly crystals
300 ml/½ pint diet fizzy apple drink

Pour the boiling water into a jug or bowl, sprinkle over the jelly crystals and stir until completely dissolved.

Slowly pour the apple drink into the jelly, stirring continuously. Allow to cool, then put into the fridge to set.

note for vegetarians:

If using vegetarian sugar-free jelly crystals (e.g. Green's Looney Tunes), read manufacturer's instructions first. If so instructed, first mix jelly crystals to a paste with 100 ml/3½ fl oz cold water, then add 200 ml/⅓ pint boiling water, stirring until completely dissolved. Then proceed as above.

Rhubarb Fool

Serves

INGREDIENTS

200 g/7 oz rhubarb
200g pot virtually fat-free
  natural fromage frais
3 tbsp granulated sweetener, or to taste
Few drops vanilla essence or extract

* This recipe uses the equivalent of half Every Day Bonus milk/yoghurt allowance per serving. If not using this allowance, count 2 Checks 0g fat per serving.

Trim the rhubarb and cut into chunks. Place in a saucepan with 1 dspn water and cook gently until soft, stirring frequently. Alternatively, microwave on high in a covered dish approximately 1½-2 minutes. Allow to cool completely.

When the rhubarb is cold, drain off excess liquid. Stir the fromage frais into the rhubarb, breaking up any chunks with a fork, until smooth.

Stir in granulated sweetener and vanilla essence or extract to taste and pour into 2 glasses or serving dishes.

Rhubarb & Orange Jelly

Serves

INGREDIENTS

200 g/7 oz rhubarb
Good pinch of ground ginger
2 dspn granulated sweetener, or to taste
300 ml/½ pint boiling water
1 sachet orange flavour sugar-free jelly crystals

Trim the rhubarb and cut into chunks. Place in a saucepan with 1 dspn water and cook gently until tender but still chunky. Alternatively, microwave on high in a covered dish approximately 1-1½ minutes or until tender but still in chunks. Stir in the ground ginger and granulated sweetener.

Pour the boiling water into a jug or bowl, sprinkle over the jelly crystals and stir until completely dissolved.

Stir the rhubarb into the jelly, allow to cool, then put in the fridge until set.

Jelly Foam

Serves 4

INGREDIENTS

1 sachet sugar-free jelly crystals, any flavour

2 egg whites (see note below)

nb:

This recipe contains raw egg white. Although Lion Quality eggs have been shown to be virtually salmonella-free, it is still recommended that pregnant women, babies and young children, the elderly or anyone with a compromised immune system should avoid raw or undercooked eggs.

Place jelly crystals in a bowl and pour on 300ml/½ pint boiling water. Stir thoroughly to dissolve. Stir in 150ml/¼ pint cold water. Allow to cool, but not set.

When jelly is cool, whisk egg whites in a large bowl to form stiff peaks. Start by stirring 2 tbsp jelly into the egg whites (not the other way round). Gradually add remaining jelly, stirring thoroughly. Egg whites should have jelly stirred into them, but will still float to the top.

Either level foam evenly over the top and leave to set, or spoon into 4-6 glasses or individual serving dishes ensuring foam is equally divided and levelled over the top before allowing to set.

Pink Cloud

Serves 1

INGREDIENTS

150-175g/5-6 oz cooked rhubarb*

1 egg white

1 dspn heat-stable granulated sweetener

* Rhubarb should be cooked either with water and sweetener, or in a little low-calorie orange squash. Alternatively, Hartley's No Added Sugar, Solid Pack canned rhubarb may be used. Put required amount into dish and sprinkle with 1-2 tsp sweetener before covering with topping.

Pre-heat oven to hottest setting.

Put cooked rhubarb into an ovenproof dish. Whisk egg white until stiff. Fold in sweetener and spread over rhubarb.

Bake in hot oven 7-8 minutes until crisp and golden. Eat right away!

No-Check

Baby Meringues

Makes **8**

INGREDIENTS

1 egg white
2 level tbsp heat-stable granulated
sweetener (e.g. Splenda)

Pre-heat oven to 110°C/gas mark ½

Using an electric whisk on high speed, whisk egg white until fairly stiff. Add sweetener and continue to whisk at slow speed until standing in peaks.

Spoon out 8 heaped teaspoons of the mixture onto a baking tray lined with baking parchment or Release non-stick foil. Bake approximately 1 hour or until crisp and dry.

Use as a snack or to garnish desserts.

No-Check

Sweet Spiced Squash

Serves **4** *to* **6**

INGREDIENTS

900g/2 lb approx. butternut squash
4 tbsp granulated sweetener, or to taste
1 tsp cinnamon, or to taste

Peel squash and remove seeds. Cut into chunks.

Boil in unsalted water until tender. Allow to cool a little, drain reserving the cooking liquid.

Place chunks in blender together with sweetener and cinnamon and blend in short bursts to a smooth, thick purée. Stir with a fork between bursts. Add a little of the cooking liquid if necessary, but take care as you don't want to end up with soup!

For a treat, serve topped with an ice-cream-scoop-size swirl of half-fat aerosol cream. Count 1 Check 2g fat.

nb:

This recipe has hints of American pumpkin pie. We've used butternut squash rather than pumpkin as it is more often available in the UK, but around Halloween time, you might want to try it using pumpkin.

No-Check
Drinks

Rhubarb & Ginger Ale Smoothie

Serves

INGREDIENTS

150g/5 oz Hartley's No Added Sugar Solid Pack canned rhubarb*

1 tbsp granulated sweetener, or to taste

150ml/¼ pint low-calorie American ginger ale

Place rhubarb, sweetener and ginger ale in a blender and whizz until smooth.

Alternatively use fresh rhubarb that has been cooked either with the minimum amount of water and sweetener to taste, or in a little low-calorie orange squash.

---

using Every Day Bonus fruit* and milk*

Peach Smoothie

Serves

INGREDIENTS

2 large or 3 medium halves canned peaches in juice, drained

150ml/¼ pint skimmed milk

1-2 tsp granulated sweetener to taste

Place peaches and milk in a blender and whizz until smooth. Stir in sweetener to taste.

* Peaches are equivalent to 1 average serving Every Day Bonus fruit. Milk is equivalent to half Every Day Bonus allowance.

If not using Every Day Bonus, count 2 Checks for peaches and 2 Checks for milk.

Mint Tea

 Serves **4**

Ideal if you have plenty of mint growing in the garden! Mint tea may help relieve flatulence and heartburn.

INGREDIENTS

40g/1½ oz fresh mint leaves
600ml/1 pint boiling water

Wash and chop mint leaves, removing any tough stems as you go. Place in a heatproof container and pour on boiling water.

Cover and leave to infuse 10 minutes. Strain through a sieve. Dilute with additional boiling water if brew is too strong for your liking.

Tea will keep for 2 days in the fridge and can be gently re-heated.

Fresh Lemonade

Serves **2** to **3**

INGREDIENTS

1 large lemon
600ml/1 pint ice-cold water
1-2 tbsp granulated sweetener,
**   or to taste**

Cut lemon in half and remove pips. Squeeze out all the juice and flesh into a jug (a lemon squeezer makes it easy!).

Pour on ice-cold water (or add 6 ice cubes and 450ml/¾ pint water). Stir in granulated sweetener to taste.

variation:

Use pink grapefruit or lime juice and sparkling mineral water to give a different taste and fizz!

No-Check

Tomato Cocktail

Serves

INGREDIENTS

- 400g can chopped tomatoes
- 2 dspn fresh lime juice
- Few drops Worcestershire sauce, to taste
- 1 tsp granulated sweetener
- Pinch of salt
- Several drops hot pepper sauce (e.g. Tabasco), to taste
- 4 ice cubes
- Mint leaves and lime slices to garnish

Place the tomatoes, lime juice and Worcestershire sauce in a blender and blitz until smooth.

Place a fine mesh sieve over a jug and press the tomatoes through with the back of a spoon to remove seeds. Scrape purée from bottom of sieve into jug.

Stir in sweetener, salt and hot pepper sauce to taste.

Serve over ice, garnished with mint leaves and a slice of lime.

No-Check *using Every Day Bonus*

Carrot, Apple & Lemon Refresher

Serves

INGREDIENTS

- 2 carrots
- 1 apple
- 4 tbsp no-added-sugar lemon squash
- 200-300 ml/ 1/3-½ pint cold water
- 1 dspn granulated sweetener, or to taste

Peel the carrots, cut into chunks and microwave on high in a covered dish approximately 2 minutes, or until just tender. Allow to cool.

Peel and core the apple and roughly chop. Place in a blender together with the carrots, lemon squash and 200 ml/⅓ pint water.

Blitz until smooth. Add more water if too thick and blitz again. Check taste and, if required, stir in granulated sweetener. Chill in the fridge.

* This recipe uses the equivalent of one-quarter of Every Day Bonus fruit allowance per serving. If not using this allowance, count 1 Check 0g fat per serving.

Plum Smoothie

Serves **1**

INGREDIENTS

3 medium or 2 large plums
150 ml/¼ pint cold skimmed milk
Pinch of cinnamon
1-2 tsp granulated sweetener

Wash plums, cut in half and remove stones. Microwave on high 1 minute in a covered dish or glass. Allow to cool 5 minutes (or longer).

Place plums, milk and cinnamon into a blender and whiz until smooth. Add granulated sweetener to taste. Drink immediately or refrigerate to chill.

This recipe uses the equivalent of half Every Day Bonus fruit allowance and half milk/yoghurt allowance. If not using this allowance, count 2 Checks 0g fat for the fruit and 2 Checks 0g fat for the milk.

Lassi

Serves **1**

This popular Indian drink is something like a savoury Slush Puppy!

INGREDIENTS

3-4 ice cubes
125g pot virtually fat-free natural yoghurt
Pinch of salt
Pinch of cumin
1 tsp lemon juice
1 tsp chopped mint leaves

Place the ice cubes in a blender and blitz in a few short bursts to roughly break up.

Add all remaining ingredients and blitz a few seconds more.

This recipe uses the equivalent of half Every Day Bonus milk/yoghurt allowance. If not using this allowance, count 2 Checks 0g fat for the whole recipe.

Low-Check
Main Courses

up to **6** *checks*

Chicken Pizzaiola

Serves **2**

INGREDIENTS

2 x 125g/4½ oz skinless chicken breasts
Spray oil
1 small onion, chopped
1 clove garlic, crushed
200g/7 oz canned tomatoes, chopped
1 tsp tomato purée
Pinch of Italian Seasoning or dried oregano
2 button mushrooms, finely chopped
1 tbsp fresh or frozen chopped parsley
Pinch of granulated sweetener
Salt and black pepper
1 tsp capers (optional)

Cook chicken breasts in pan sprayed with oil approximately 20-25 minutes, or until cooked through. Turn half-way through cooking time.

Spray a small saucepan with oil and cook onions gently until softened. Add garlic and cook 1 minute. Stir in tomatoes, tomato purée and Italian seasoning or oregano. Simmer gently, uncovered, 10-15 minutes, stirring now and again, until sauce has thickened and reduced. Stir in mushrooms and cook 1 minute. Stir in parsley, sweetener, salt and pepper to taste. Stir in capers if using.

Serve each person with 1 cooked chicken breast topped with half the sauce.

per serving
155 6 2 Turkey Schnitzel

Serves 1

INGREDIENTS

100g/3 oz turkey breast steak
Salt and pepper
1 small slice bread
(or remove crusts from 1 medium slice)
½ tsp mixed herbs
A little skimmed milk
Spray oil
Lemon wedges to serve

Put turkey steak between two layers of clingfilm and beat out until it is ½ cm/¼ inch thick. Season lightly.

Make bread into crumbs and season with salt, pepper and herbs.

Brush turkey with skimmed milk, then coat with seasoned crumbs. Cover and chill in fridge at least 30 minutes.

When ready to cook, spray pan with oil and heat. Cook turkey over moderate heat approximately 5-6 minutes each side or until golden and cooked through.

Serve hot with lemon wedges, or cold, cut into strips, with salad.

nb:

For a change, you can add ½ tsp finely grated lemon zest and plenty of black pepper to the breadcrumbs for a lemon pepper flavour.

Red Pepper Chicken Spirals   *Serves* **1**

INGREDIENTS

½ red pepper
150 g/5 oz chicken or turkey breast fillet
Salt and freshly ground black pepper
2 basil leaves, shredded
Spray oil
Snow peas or mangetout
Cherry tomatoes

Pre-heat oven to 200°C/gas mark 6.

Place the red pepper under a hot grill and cook until the skin is blistered and slightly charred.

Peel away the skin and remove any ribs and seeds.

Place the chicken or turkey breast between clingfilm and beat with a rolling pin to flatten it out evenly.

Place the grilled red pepper on top of the flattened chicken or turkey and sprinkle with basil. Season lightly with salt and pepper, and roll up firmly into a cylinder.

Place in a baking pan that has been sprayed lightly with oil and cook in the pre-heated oven for about 25 minutes until the chicken or turkey is thoroughly cooked.

Slice the roll diagonally and serve hot with cooked snow peas or mangetout and grilled cherry tomatoes.

75 **3** **1** Vegetable Spring Rolls

Makes **4**

INGREDIENTS

2 spring onions, sliced
60g/2 oz frozen sliced mixed peppers
Spray oil
1 small carrot, peeled and coarsely grated
1 tbsp frozen peas
85g/3 oz beansprouts
½ Oxo Chinese cube
2 x 45g large sheets filo pastry (e.g. Jus-rol)

Pre-heat oven to 200°C/gas mark 6.

Cook onions and peppers in pan sprayed with oil approximately 3 minutes. Stir in grated carrot, peas, beansprouts and crumbled ½ Chinese cube. Stir-fry 1 minute. Remove from heat.

Lay 1 filo sheet on flat surface and spray top side with oil. Place other sheet on top and cut, down and across, into 4 rectangles.

Put quarter of the vegetable mixture at the short end of each piece of pastry. Roll up each piece, tucking in sides.

Place rolls on a non-stick baking tray and spray lightly with oil. Bake approximately 20 minutes, until golden.

155 **6** **4** Mexican Steak Strips

Serves **1**

INGREDIENTS

125g/4½ oz lean, trimmed rump steak
1 red or green pepper or a good handful
  frozen mixed peppers
1 shallot or small onion
60g/2 oz mushrooms
Spray oil
½ tsp chilli powder, or to taste
Pinch of cumin
Salt and black pepper

Cut the steak into small strips. Slice the pepper, shallot and mushrooms.

Stir-fry the steak strips in pan sprayed with oil. Remove steak.

Add vegetables to pan and stir-fry 3-4 minutes. Sprinkle in chilli and cumin and stir-fry 1 minute more. Return steak to pan together with 1 dspn water and stir-fry 2-3 minutes more. Season to taste.

per serving
150 **6** **2** # Honey & Lemon Chicken Skewers

Serves **1**

INGREDIENTS

- 100 g/3½ oz skinless chicken or turkey breast
- 1 ring pineapple in juice, drained
- ½ pepper, any colour
- 1 tsp runny honey
- 1 tsp lemon juice
- ½ tsp soy sauce

Cut the chicken into 6-8 cubes. Cut the pineapple into 6 pieces and the pepper into 6 squares.

Mix together the honey, lemon juice and soy sauce and turn the chicken cubes in the mixture to coat. Leave to marinate at least 15 minutes.

If using bamboo skewers, soak 2 in water at least 15 minutes to prevent scorching.

Thread the skewers with alternating pieces of chicken, pepper and pineapple.

Grill under a pre-heated hot grill approximately 15-20 minutes, turning now and again, until the chicken is cooked through and the pepper is slightly charred at the edges.

per serving
125 **5** **3** # Sherried Kidneys

Serves **1**

INGREDIENTS

- 2 lamb's kidneys
- 60g/2 oz mushrooms
- 150ml/¼ pint beef stock
- 1 tbsp sherry
- 1 tbsp tomato purée
- Pinch of mixed herbs

Wash kidneys, remove and discard inner core. This is easily done with kitchen scissors. Roughly chop or snip flesh.

Place kidneys in a pan together with remaining ingredients. Bring to a gentle simmer ensuring that tomato purée is stirred in.

Continue to simmer 10-15 minutes, stirring occasionally.

150 6 2 Sausages in Red Wine Gravy

Serves

INGREDIENTS

2 Wall's Lean Recipe Sausages *
1 small onion, sliced
Spray oil
½ Bovril cube
100ml/3½ fl.oz hot water
1 tsp tomato purée
2 tbsp red wine

Other brand very-low-calorie sausages may be used, up to 70 calories per sausage.

Grill the sausages.

Cook onions slowly in pan sprayed with oil until soft and starting to brown. Add a little water if necessary to help soften and prevent sticking.

Dissolve stock cube in hot water.

Stir tomato purée into onions and cook 30 seconds. Add wine and allow to bubble up. Add stock and boil to reduce a little.

Add sausages to pan and simmer 2 minutes.

---

155 6 4 Steak Diane

Serves

INGREDIENTS

2 x 100g/3½ oz lean, thin rump steaks or "quick-fry" steaks
Salt and black pepper
Spray oil
1 small onion, finely chopped
4 tbsp white wine
1 heaped tbsp fat-free natural fromage frais

Season steaks with salt and black pepper.

Spray pan with oil and cook onions gently until starting to soften, stirring frequently. Push onions to one side of pan, turn up heat, add steaks and cook 2-3 minutes each side, or to your liking. Remove steaks to serving plates.

Add wine to pan and allow to bubble up, stirring and scraping in onions and pan juices, about 30 seconds to 1 minute. Take pan off heat and stir in fromage frais.

Serve each person with 1 steak topped with half the sauce.

160 6 6 Steak & Mushroom 'Sandwich'

Serves 1

INGREDIENTS

100 g/3½ oz lean fillet steak, all fat removed
2 very large portobello (saucer) mushrooms
Spray oil
1 garlic clove, crushed
Salt and freshly ground black pepper

Herb pesto:

1 tbsp virtually fat-free fromage frais
Few sprigs of parsley, finely chopped
Few sprigs of basil, finely chopped
2 ripe cherry tomatoes, skinned and finely chopped
Salt and freshly ground black pepper

Season the steak with salt and pepper and cook under a pre-heated hot grill according to taste - about 3-5 minutes each side, depending on whether you like it rare or well done.

Meanwhile, remove the stalks from the portobello mushrooms and spray each mushroom lightly with oil. Grill, rounded side uppermost, until golden and softened and then turn the mushrooms over, place the crushed garlic in the middle and grill until cooked on top.

Mix together all the ingredients for the herb pesto.

On a serving plate, place a cooked mushroom and smear with a little of the pesto. Arrange the steak on top and spread with the remaining pesto. Cover with the other mushroom to create a 'sandwich'.

Serve immediately with No-Check salad or steamed green vegetables.

Moroccan Meatballs

Serves **1**

INGREDIENTS

100 g/3½ oz lean lamb, minced
½ small onion, grated or finely chopped
Pinch each of ground cumin, cayenne and paprika
Pinch each of ground cinnamon and cloves
Few mint leaves, finely chopped
Few sprigs coriander, finely chopped
Salt and freshly ground black pepper

Harissa Salsa:

1 large ripe tomato, finely diced
¼ red onion, finely chopped
Juice of ½ lime
Dash of harissa paste
Chopped fresh mint or coriander

In a bowl, mix together the minced lamb, onion, ground spices and chopped herbs. Season with a little salt and pepper.

Shape the mixture into little balls and thread them on to a skewer, shaping them around the skewer.

Cook under a pre-heated hot grill, turning the skewer frequently, for about 10 minutes, until cooked and golden brown.

Meanwhile, make the salsa. In a small bowl, mix together the diced tomato and onion. Add the lime juice and a tiny blob of harissa - it is very hot indeed so use sparingly and add more if wished. Stir in the chopped herbs and check the seasoning.

Serve the hot meatballs with the salsa and a crisp No-Check salad tossed in oil-free dressing.

tip:

To make this dish more substantial, serve the meatballs, salsa in a small wholemeal pitta bread. Add 5 Checks.

145 6 5 Deep South Ham in Cola

Serves 2

Inspired by Nigella Lawson

INGREDIENTS

2 lean, unsmoked gammon steaks,
   approx. 125g/4½ oz each after trimming visible fat
1 shallot or small onion sliced
150ml/¼ pint diet cola
1 tsp French mustard
½ tsp granulated sweetener

Put the gammon steaks and onions into a shallow dish and pour over the diet cola. Cover and leave to marinate at least 1 hour.

Transfer everything to a saucepan. Bring to a simmer, cover and simmer very gently approximately 30 minutes or until gammon is cooked through and tender.

Remove steaks from pan and transfer to grill rack. Mix together mustard and sweetener and spread over steaks. Grill under moderate heat 1 minute.

nb:

Liquid left in the pan may be chilled, any surface fat skimmed and discarded, and the remaining stock added to a No-Check vegetable soup. If steaks were well trimmed before cooking, there will hardly be any fat to discard.

per serving

145 6 4 5-Spice Pork Stir-fry

Serves

INGREDIENTS

100g/3½ oz lean pork or pork stir-fry
1 tbsp light soy sauce
1 tbsp sherry
½ tsp Chinese 5-spice powder
Spray oil
250g/9 oz mixture of chopped fresh
  or frozen vegetables

e.g.:

fresh spring onions, carrot shavings, sliced
  peppers and beansprouts

or:

frozen chopped cabbage, sliced/chopped onions,
  sliced carrots, sliced mixed peppers, sliced
  green beans.

If not already done, cut the pork into small
strips. Mix together the soy sauce, sherry
and 5-spice powder and marinate the pork
in the mixture 15 minutes.

Spray pan with oil and stir-fry the pork
strips approximately 5 minutes until cooked
through. Remove from pan.

Add vegetables to pan and stir-fry a few
minutes until just tender. Fresh vegetables
may need a little water to prevent them
from sticking, but there is usually sufficient
moisture in frozen vegetables.

Return pork strips to pan together with
marinade and stir-fry 2 minutes more.

---

per serving

150 6 1 Honey, Lemon & Garlic Turkey

Serves

INGREDIENTS

115g/4 oz turkey breast
1 tsp honey
1 dspn lemon juice
1 small clove garlic, crushed
Salt
Spray oil

Cut turkey into 2 thin escalopes. If necessary, beat
out to flatten

Mix together the honey, lemon and garlic in a shallow dish.
Use to coat the escalopes and leave to marinate
15 minutes. Season lightly with salt.

Spray pan with oil and heat. Cook the escalopes over
medium heat, approximately 1½ minutes each side, or until
cooked through but not dried out.

Normandy Pork

Serves **2**

INGREDIENTS

2 x 115g/4 oz pork escalopes
1 small onion, sliced thinly
1 small Cox's apple, cored and sliced
Spray oil
1 chicken Oxo cube
100ml/3½ fl.oz hot water
½ tsp mild mustard
1 rounded tbsp fat-free fromage frais

Beat out escalopes until ½ cm/¼ inch thick.

Cook onions gently in a non-stick pan sprayed with oil until soft and starting to colour. Add a little water if necessary to prevent sticking. Add apple slices and cook 5-7 minutes until softened and starting to colour, occasionally stirring and turning over apple slices. Remove from pan.

Re-spray pan and cook escalopes over moderate heat about 3 minutes each side, or until cooked through.

Dissolve stock cube in hot water.

Return apples and onions to pan with pork. Pour over stock and stir mustard in thoroughly. Simmer 2 minutes turning over escalopes now and again.

Remove pan from heat, tilt pan and stir fromage frais thoroughly into juices.

Serve half the recipe to each person.

160 6 4 Pork with Pineapple & Spring Onion

Serves 2

INGREDIENTS

1 garlic clove, crushed
1 tbsp light soy sauce
1 tbsp sherry
1 tsp granulated sweetener
Pinch of ground ginger
175 g/6 oz well trimmed, lean pork cubes
Spray oil
4 spring onions, trimmed and sliced
Good handful of frozen sliced green beans
2 rings pineapple in juice, drained and
   cut into chunks
150 g/5 oz beansprouts

Mix together the garlic, soy sauce, sherry, sweetener and ginger in a shallow dish. If pork cubes are large, cut into smaller strips. Marinate the pork cubes in the mixture at least 15 minutes.

Spray a pan or wok with oil and heat. Remove the pork from the marinade, reserving the marinade. Stir-fry the pork cubes 3 minutes, then add the spring onions and stir-fry a further 1 minute.

Add the green beans and stir-fry 2 minutes.

Add the pineapple, beansprouts and remaining marinade and cook a further 2 minutes.

Serve half the recipe to each person.

150 6 2 Bacon & Potato Oven Hash

Serves 1

INGREDIENTS

150g boiled potato, diced
1 small onion, chopped
2 bacon medallions
3 cherry tomatoes
Spray oil
Salt and pepper

Spread the diced potato and chopped onion over a baking tray, spray lightly with oil and bake in a pre-heated hot oven for 10 minutes.

Add chopped bacon medallions and cherry tomatoes and bake for 10-15 minutes more.

Stir together, season to taste and serve.

75 **3 ❶ Fisherman's Stew** *Serves* **4**

Courtesy of Class Manager Lorraine Queen

1 medium onion, chopped

1 clove garlic, crushed

Spray oil

Pinch each of mixed herbs, oregano and chilli powder

1 tbsp white wine

1 fish stock cube

600ml/1 pint hot water

400g can chopped tomatoes

2 tbsp tomato purée

60g/2 oz carrots, diced

2 small new potatoes, diced

100g/3½ oz smoked whiting or smoked cod

20g/ ¾ oz smoked salmon

100g/3½ oz prawns, defrosted if frozen

Soften onion and garlic in a saucepan sprayed with oil, over medium heat. Stir in herbs, chilli powder and wine and simmer gently 2 minutes.

Dissolve stock cube in hot water. Stir tomatoes and tomato purée into saucepan, followed by the stock, potatoes and carrots. Simmer 15 minutes, stirring now and again.

Microwave the smoked whiting or cod 1 minute, then flake gently with your fingertips to ensure any bones are removed. Add to saucepan together with the smoked salmon. Simmer 5 minutes, add the prawns and simmer a further 5 minutes.

Serve one-quarter of the recipe to each person.

120 5 3 Italian Cod Steak

Serves

INGREDIENTS

Spray oil
1 onion, finely sliced
1 garlic clove, crushed
½ red pepper, deseeded and thinly sliced
200 g/7 oz canned chopped tomatoes
115 g/4 oz cod steak
5 stoned black olives
Salt and freshly ground black pepper
Chopped parsley, to garnish

Spray a pan lightly with oil and place over a low heat. Add the onion, garlic and red pepper and cook gently until they are really softened.

Pour in the tomatoes and simmer gently for 5 minutes.

Add the cod steak and the olives, then cover the pan and cook very gently over a low heat for 20-25 minutes, until the cod is cooked and the sauce reduced.

Season to taste with salt and pepper and sprinkle with chopped parsley. Serve hot with steamed green No-Check vegetables.

150 6 5 Pesto Fish Parcels

Serves

INGREDIENTS

150g/5 oz cod, haddock or other white fish fillet
1 level tsp pesto
3-4 thinly sliced rings of onion
1 small tomato, thinly sliced
1-2 mushrooms, sliced
Black pepper
1-2 basil leaves (optional)

Pre-heat oven to 180°C/gas mark 4.

Place the fish on a square of greaseproof paper large enough to enclose it, then place fish and greaseproof paper onto a similar size square of foil.

Spread the pesto over the fish and top with onion, tomato and mushroom slices. Sprinkle with black pepper and lay on basil leaves, if using.

Make the greaseproof paper and foil into a secure parcel and place on a baking tray. Bake approximately 20 minutes

per serving

160 6 2 Haddock with Citrus Sauce Serves 2

INGREDIENTS

2 x 150g/5 oz haddock fillets
1 tsp cornflour
125ml/4½ fl.oz unsweetened orange juice
½ tsp vegetable stock granules (e.g. Marigold)
1 tbsp freshly chopped parsley or mint
A squeeze of lemon juice

Poach, steam or microwave fish.

Place cornflour in a saucepan and stir in a little of the orange juice to form a smooth paste. Stir in stock granules and remaining juice.

Bring to the boil stirring continuously until thickened. Stir in herbs and lemon juice to taste.

Serve each person with 1 portion of fish with half the sauce poured over.

---

per serving

150 6 1 Haddock Fillet with Orange & Chilli Glaze Serves 1

INGREDIENTS

Spray oil
150 g/5 oz haddock fillet
Grated zest and juice of ½ large juicy orange
1 spring onion, finely shredded
1 tsp sweet chilli sauce
1-2 pak choi
Dash of soy sauce
Chopped flat-leaf parsley to garnish

Pre-heat oven to 180°C/gas mark 4.

Lightly spray a baking dish with oil, place the haddock fillet in it and cook in the oven 5 minutes.

In a small bowl, mix together the orange zest and juice with the shredded spring onion and chilli sauce.

Remove the haddock from the oven and brush with the orange glaze.

Continue cooking for 10 minutes more until the haddock is cooked, opaque and flakes easily.

Meanwhile, steam the pak choi until just tender. Sprinkle with soy sauce and serve with the haddock, sprinkling the fish with some chopped parsley.

per serving
70 3 0 Vegetable & Pasta Lunch Bowl

Serves 4

Courtesy of member Sandra Almond, Accrington

INGREDIENTS

1 onion, chopped
1 leek, sliced
1 stick celery, chopped
2 carrots, diced
2 cloves garlic, crushed
600ml/1 pint chicken stock
200g canned chopped tomatoes
60g/2 oz frozen peas
60g/2 oz soup pasta
1 tsp caster sugar
1dspn dried parsley
1 dspn dried basil
Salt and pepper

Put onion, leek, celery, carrots and garlic into a large saucepan and add chicken stock. Bring to the boil, then simmer 10 minutes.

Add tomatoes and peas and bring back to the boil. Add pasta, sugar, herbs and seasoning to taste. Simmer until pasta is tender, stirring now and again.

Serve one-quarter of the recipe to each person.

per serving
150 6 7 Spanish Tuna Salad

Serves 2

Courtesy of Class Assistant Jaqui McIntosh, Edinburgh

INGREDIENTS

1 small carrot, chopped
1 red pepper, de-seeded and chopped into chunks
1 tbsp frozen peas
1 hard-boiled egg, cooled and chopped
85-100g can tuna in brine, drained
60g/2 oz cooked prawns or seafood mix,
    defrosted if frozen
2 tbsp low-calorie mayonnaise
1 clove garlic, finely chopped.

Cook carrot in boiling water. When almost tender, add peppers and peas and cook 2 minutes. Drain and cool.

Mix vegetables with chopped egg, flaked tuna and prawns.

Mix mayonnaise with garlic and stir through salad mixture.

Serve half the recipe to each person.

150 6 2 Pasta Brunch

Serves 1

INGREDIENTS

30g/1 oz pasta shapes
Spray oil
1 small onion, chopped
2 turkey rashers, chopped
1 tomato, chopped
2-3 mushrooms, sliced

Cook pasta in lightly salted boiling water until just tender.

Spray pan with oil and cook onions until softened. Add chopped turkey rashers, mushrooms and tomatoes and cook until browned.

Drain pasta and stir into turkey mixture.

---

125 5 3 Really Low Savoury Quorn Pie

Serves 1

INGREDIENTS

225g/8 oz cauliflower florets
1 small onion, chopped
1 medium carrot, chopped
1 large stick celery, finely sliced
1 level tbsp Oxo Vegetable
  Gravy Granules
100-150ml/4-5 fl.oz boiling water
100g/3 ½ oz Quorn
  Pieces or Mince
Black pepper

Boil cauliflower until fairly soft. Drain and mash.

Place the onion, carrot and celery into a medium pan with 2 tbsp water. Cover and cook gently 5-10 minutes until softened and starting to colour. Check now and again and if necessary stir in another tablespoon of water to prevent sticking.

Mix gravy granules with boiling water, stirring well, until you have a smooth gravy.

Add Quorn to vegetables in pan and pour over gravy. Cook gently, stirring continuously 3-5 minutes. Transfer to a heat-proof dish.

Pre-heat grill to hot. Spread the mashed cauliflower over the Quorn mixture and sprinkle with black pepper. Brown lightly under the grill.

145 6 1 Warm Pasta & Crabstick Salad

Serves

Courtesy of Your Dietline Member Corinne Kay

INGREDIENTS

30 g/1 oz pasta shapes or rice
3 crabsticks
Oil-free French dressing

Cook the pasta in lightly salted boiling water until just tender. Drain.

Cut the crabsticks into 3 or 4 pieces each and add to the warm pasta.

Pour a little oil-free French dressing over and stir well. Eat warm accompanied by No-Check salad.

tip:

Make double the quantity and store half in the fridge – it is equally good served cold.

---

150 6 2 Orange & Soy Quorn Fillets

Serves

INGREDIENTS

2 frozen Quorn Fillets (uncoated)
75ml/5 tbsp unsweetened orange juice
1 tsp soy sauce
½ tsp granulated sweetener
½ tsp cornflour
A few finely chopped mint leaves (optional)

Place fillets, orange juice and soy sauce in a small pan and heat gently until completely thawed and warmed through. Turn fillets frequently.

Remove fillets to serving dish.

Stir sweetener into juice. Mix cornflour with 1 tbsp water and stir thoroughly into juice approximately 20 seconds.

If using, stir chopped mint into sauce. Pour sauce over fillets.

150 6 4 Roasted Vegetable Wrap

Serves 2

INGREDIENTS

1 pepper, any colour
1 courgette
1 onion
2 tomatoes
Spray oil
Salt and black pepper
Pinch of mixed herbs
2 flour tortillas
2 tbsp virtually fat-free fromage frais
Few drops hot pepper sauce (optional)

Pre-heat oven to 200°C/gas mark 6.

Cut the pepper into eighths and remove the seeds. Slice the courgette thickly. Cut the onion into wedges and cut the tomatoes into quarters.

Spray a baking tray lightly with oil and spread the vegetables over. Season with salt, plenty of black pepper and a pinch of mixed herbs. Spray lightly with oil and roast in pre-heated oven approximately 25 minutes until starting to char at the edges.

Spread half the vegetables over each tortilla and spread 1tbsp fromage frais down the centre of each.

Sprinkle over a few drops of hot pepper sauce, if using, and roll up the tortillas, folding in the sides.

Serve 1 tortilla wrap to each person, cut diagonally in half.

150 6 5 Corned Beef & Hoisin Wrappers

Serves 1

INGREDIENTS

5cm/2" piece of cucumber
1 spring onion
50g/1¾ oz Princes Lean Corned Beef
A few lettuce leaves, preferably cos, Romaine or Little Gem
2 rounded tsp, hoisin or plum sauce

Cut the cucumber into strips. Cut the spring onion lengthways into strips. Cut the corned beef into small cubes.

Arrange all the ingredients on a plate. Take a lettuce leaf, place on some spring onion and cucumber, then some corned beef and a dab or two of sauce. Wrap lettuce around the filling and eat.

Continue until everything is eaten!

160 6 6 Stuffed Courgettes

Serves 2

Courtesy of class member Frances Mair

INGREDIENTS

4 medium courgettes
1 carrot, chopped
1 small onion, chopped
3-4 mushrooms, chopped
1 small red pepper, deseeded and chopped
1 garlic clove, crushed
Spray oil
Pinch of mixed herbs
Salt and pepper
2 medium slices bread, made into crumbs
60 g/2 oz mature half-fat cheddar, grated

Pre-heat oven to 200°C/gas mark 6.

Top and tail the courgettes, cut lengthwise, scoop out and reserve the centres. Place the courgette shells on a plate and microwave on high until just tender. Place in a baking dish.

Chop the reserved centres of the courgettes and stir-fry in a pan sprayed with oil together with the remaining vegetables and garlic. Stir-fry until softened and season to taste with mixed herbs, salt and pepper.

Pile the vegetables into the centres of the courgettes. Mix together the breadcrumbs and cheese and place on top of the vegetables. Spray lightly with oil.

Bake in pre-heated oven approximately 15 minutes until the breadcrumbs and cheese are golden.

Caramelised Tomato & Onion Pitta

Serves **1**

Courtesy of Your Dietline Member Corinne Kay

INGREDIENTS

4-6 tomatoes cut into thick slices
Spray oil
2 large onions, thinly sliced
1 dspn brown sugar
1 medium pitta bread (per serving)

Pre-heat oven to 200°C/gas mark 6.

Place the tomato slices on a baking tray and roast in pre-heated oven 10-15 minutes until just starting to char at the edges.

Spray a pan with oil and spread the onions over the base. Cook over gentle heat, stirring now and again, approximately 15-20 minutes, until the onions are softened and starting to colour. Add the brown sugar and stir until dissolved.

To serve, warm the pitta bread in the oven or under the grill, spread over some of the onion mixture and top with the tomatoes.

The remaining onions and tomatoes can be stored covered in the fridge 2-3 days and can be spread over pitta bread or toast slices and served cold or warmed under the grill.

tip:

When roasting the tomatoes, think about roasting some other vegetables, such as peppers or courgettes, so you make good use of the oven and save time making other recipes.

Low-Check
Complete Meals
up to **12** *checks*

per serving
305 **12** **8**

Red Pesto Chicken with Pan-fried Courgettes & New Potatoes

Serves **1**

1 medium skinless chicken breast
1 button mushroom, finely chopped
1 level dspn red pesto (e.g. Bertolli Pesto Rosso)
1 turkey rasher
150g/5 oz new potatoes, boiled
1 medium courgette, sliced
Spray oil

Pre-heat oven to 180°C/gas mark 4.

Cut chicken breast horizontally almost in half and open out like a book. Place chopped mushrooms and pesto on one side and fold over other side to cover.

Wrap turkey rasher around chicken breast and secure with 1 or 2 cocktail sticks. Place in a shallow ovenproof dish and bake, uncovered 25 minutes, until cooked through.

Meanwhile, cut boiled new potatoes in half. Spray pan with oil and heat. Place potatoes on one side of pan, cut side down, and spread courgette slices over remaining base of pan. Cook over medium heat until browned underneath. Turn over potatoes and courgettes and brown other side.

Remove cocktail stick from chicken and serve with potatoes and courgettes.

300 12 2 Double Deal Chicken

Serves 1

INGREDIENTS

200g/7 oz potato, peeled and cut into three
1 onion, chopped
1 large carrot, sliced
2 sticks celery, sliced
1 skinless chicken breast
300ml/ ½ pint chicken stock
1 tbsp tomato purée
1 small courgette, sliced

Place all ingredients except courgettes into a large saucepan. Bring to a simmer, cover and cook very gently 20 minutes, stirring now and again.

With a measuring jug, remove 300ml/ ½ pint of the liquid and vegetables, excluding potatoes, and allow to cool a little.

Add courgettes to chicken and vegetables in pan, cover and cook approximately 5-10 minutes more until courgettes are tender.

Meanwhile, roughly crush or liquidise the removed liquid and vegetables to serve as a soup first course.

Serve chicken breast, potatoes and remaining vegetables as your second course.

310 12 10 Chicken & Potato Curry

Serves 2

INGREDIENTS

2 medium skinless chicken breasts
1 onion, sliced
Spray oil
2 level tbsp Korma curry paste (e.g. Patak's)
200g/7 oz peeled weight potatoes, cut into 20 cubes
400g can tomatoes
150g/5 oz frozen spinach

Cut chicken breasts into cubes. Spray a large saucepan with oil and stir-fry chicken and onions over high heat about 7 minutes.

Stir in curry paste and cubed potatoes and stir 1 minute more.

Stir in tomatoes and spinach. Bring to the boil, then turn down heat, cover and simmer gently approximately 30 minutes. Stir frequently, breaking up tomatoes and spinach, until potatoes are cooked.

Serve half the recipe to each person and sprinkle with a little garam masala (optional).

Spanish Orange Chicken

Serves **1**

INGREDIENTS

Spray oil
1 medium skinless, boneless chicken breast
1 small onion, thinly sliced
1 garlic clove, crushed
2-3 tablespoons sherry vinegar
100 ml/3½ fl oz chicken stock
1 juicy orange, thinly sliced
150 g/5 oz new potatoes
Salt and freshly ground black pepper
1 tbsp chopped fresh parsley

Spray a pan lightly with oil and place over medium heat. When hot, add the chicken breast and cook for a few minutes on each side until golden brown. Remove the chicken and set aside.

Add the onion and garlic to the pan and cook gently until softened.

Add the sherry vinegar and stir well, then add the chicken stock and turn up the heat. When it is boiling, reduce the heat to a simmer and add the sliced orange and chicken breast.

Cook gently for about 20 minutes until the chicken is cooked through.

Meanwhile, cook the new potatoes in lightly salted boiling water.

Check the chicken for seasoning and sprinkle with chopped parsley. Serve with new potatoes and a selection of No-Check vegetables.

per serving
250 **10** **7** # Bacon, Savoy & New Potato Pan-fry

Serves **1**

INGREDIENTS

Spray oil
85g/3 oz onion, sliced
200g/7 oz new potatoes, boiled and thickly sliced
2 rashers lean, trimmed back bacon, chopped
85g/3 oz savoy cabbage leaves, shredded
Black pepper

Spray pan with oil and cook onions over moderate heat. Stir occasionally and add a little water if necessary to prevent sticking.

Turn up heat a little and add potatoes and bacon. Allow to cook stirring frequently, but not all the time. This gives the potatoes a chance to brown.

Add cabbage and 1 tbsp water. Stir-fry until cabbage just starts to wilt. Season with plenty of black pepper.

300 **12** ④ Bacon & Apple Mix Up

Serves ①

INGREDIENTS

Spray oil
1 onion, sliced
1 eating apple, cored and cut into wedges
4 bacon medallions, roughly chopped
200 g/7 oz new potatoes, boiled and sliced thickly

Spray a non-stick frying pan with oil and heat. Cook the onions until softened.

Add the apple and bacon and continue cooking, stirring frequently, until the bacon is cooked and apples are starting to colour. Remove from pan.

Re-spray the pan and heat. Spread the potato slices over the base of the pan and allow to brown underneath. Turn over and brown other side.

Return the bacon mixture to the pan and cook 1-2 minutes or until heated through, stirring frequently.

Serve with steamed cabbage and carrots, or other No-Check vegetables.

note:

If you are unable to find bacon medallions in your supermarket, simply use the lean round part from 4 back bacon rashers.

Wrapped Pork in Lemon & Wine Sauce

Serves **1**

INGREDIENTS

85 g/3 oz lean pork fillet or tenderloin
2 fresh sage leaves
1 thin slice Parma ham, fat removed
Spray oil
75 ml/2½ fl oz dry white wine
100 ml/3½ fl oz chicken stock
Juice and finely grated zest of 1 lemon
Salt and freshly ground black pepper
30 g/1 oz tagliatelle or fettuccine

Beat the pork fillet with a rolling pin to flatten it out slightly. Place 2 sage leaves on top and then wrap it in a slice of Parma ham.

Spray a pan with oil and when it is hot, add the pork and cook over medium heat until golden brown on both sides.

Add the white wine and chicken stock together with the lemon juice and zest, and cook gently for about 15 minutes until the pork is thoroughly cooked and the liquid has reduced.

Meanwhile cook the pasta in lightly salted boiling water until just tender.

Season the sauce with salt and pepper. Drain the pasta and serve with the pork and sauce together with a selection of No-Check vegetables.

310 12 7 Pork with Creamy Bacon & Mushroom Sauce

Serves 2

INGREDIENTS

300 g/10 oz potatoes
A little skimmed milk
2 x 100 g/3½ oz thin pork escalopes, all fat removed
Spray oil
2 bacon medallions, chopped
4 mushrooms, sliced
1 tbsp sherry
150 ml/¼ pint chicken stock
4 tbsp half-fat crème fraîche
Black pepper

Peel and boil the potatoes. When soft, drain and mash with a little skimmed milk.

Spray a non-stick pan with oil and heat. Add the escalopes and cook over medium heat about 3-4 minutes. Turn over and add the bacon and mushrooms to the pan. Cook a further 4-5 minutes, stirring the mushrooms and bacon now and again until the bacon is cooked.

Add the sherry and stock to the pan and simmer 2 minutes. Stir in the crème fraîche, warm through for a few seconds and season with black pepper.

Serve 1 escalope topped with half the sauce to each person together with half the mashed potato and your choice of No-Check vegetables.

note:

If you are unable to find bacon medallions in your supermarket, simply use the lean round part from 2 back bacon rashers.

300 `12` `7` Fish & Prawn Pie

Serves

INGREDIENTS

200g/7 oz potato
85g/3 oz broccoli
150g pack Ross Fish Choice Fish in Butter Sauce
30g/1 oz cooked prawns, defrosted if frozen

Boil potato. Drain, leaving a little water in the pan, then mash.

Boil or microwave broccoli, drain and chop.

Boil or microwave fish in sauce according to pack instructions.

In a grill-proof dish, mix chopped broccoli with prawns and fish in sauce. Top with mashed potato and brown under the grill.

---

300 `12` `25` Smoked Mackerel Stir-fry

Serves

INGREDIENTS

Spray oil
2 spring onions, sliced diagonally
1 small carrot, peeled and cut into thin strips
½ red pepper, deseeded and cut into thin strips
30 g/1 oz snow peas or mangetout, trimmed
1 cm/½ in piece fresh root ginger, shredded
85 g/3 oz Chinese leaves, shredded
Handful of beansprouts
85 g/3 oz smoked mackerel fillet, flaked roughly
Juice of ½ lemon
1-2 tsp soy sauce
Chopped flat-leaf parsley, to garnish

Spray a wok or deep frying pan lightly with oil and place it over a medium to high heat.

When hot, add the spring onions, carrot, red pepper, snow peas or mangetout and ginger and stir-fry briskly 1-2 minutes.

Add the Chinese leaves, beansprouts and flaked smoked mackerel and stir-fry 1 minute.

Add the lemon juice and soy sauce. Heat through and check the seasoning.

Sprinkle with parsley and serve immediately.

280 11 3 Steamed Sweet Chilli Fish & Noodles

Serves 2

INGREDIENTS

150g pack Amoy Straight to Wok Noodles
300g/10 oz skinless cod or other white fish
2 spring onions, finely sliced
2 tbsp sweet chilli sauce
No-Check vegetables to serve

Cut 2 large squares of strong foil. Put half the noodles on each piece of foil, spreading them out a little.

Cut the fish into chunks and place on top of the noodles together with the spring onions.

Top each portion with 1 tbsp sweet chilli sauce, then scrunch up the foil to make 2 well-sealed parcels. Take care not to puncture foil.

Bring 5cm/2 inches water to the boil in a pan large enough to take the two parcels. Place parcels in water, keep at a gentle boil and cook approximately 8 minutes. Remove parcels with a slotted spoon, open carefully and transfer noodles and fish onto 2 serving plates.

Serve with no-Check vegetables, either boiled, microwaved, or stir-fried in spray oil.

---

295 12 2 Prawn Noodles

Serves 1

per serving

INGREDIENTS

60g/2 oz Chinese noodles
Spray oil
2 spring onions, sliced diagonally
115g/4 oz any colour fresh or
    frozen peppers, sliced
3-4 mushrooms, sliced
85g/3 oz cooked prawns,
    defrosted if frozen

Boil noodles approximately 3 minutes then drain.

Cook spring onion, peppers and mushrooms in pan sprayed with oil until just tender.

Add prawns and noodles and heat through 1-2 minutes. Serve sprinkled with soy sauce to taste

270 **11** **10** Top Tapas

Serves **1**

Courtesy of Class Assistant Jaqui McIntosh, Edinburgh

Ideally, each recipe should be served in a separate small tapas dish - but they're equally delicious served on a plate!

per serving

80 **3** **2** Gambas al Ajillo (Garlic Prawns)

INGREDIENTS

½ tsp olive oil
60g/2 oz prawns
1 clove garlic, finely chopped

Heat oil in a pan, add prawns and garlic and stir-fry 2 minutes.

per serving

150 **6** **4** Patatas Bravas (Spicy Potatoes)

INGREDIENTS

100g McCain Home Roasts
1 dspn tomato ketchup
Dash of hot chilli sauce

Oven-bake potatoes as directed. Mix tomato ketchup with chilli sauce and spoon over potatoes.

per serving

40 **2** **4** Ensalada de pimientos rojos
(Red Pepper Salad)

INGREDIENTS

1 small red pepper, de-seeded and
   chopped into chunks
1 plum tomato, chopped into chunks
1 tsp olive oil
Dash of white wine vinegar

Mix all ingredients together.

300 12 6 Smoked Salmon
& Courgette Tagliatelle

 Serves 2

INGREDIENTS

85 g/3 oz tagliatelle
1 medium courgette, sliced
100 g/3½ oz extra light soft cheese
2-3 tbsp skimmed milk
Squeeze of lemon juice
Black pepper
125 g/4½ oz smoked salmon pieces/trimmings
2 dspn chopped fresh parsley
Wedges of lemon for serving.

Cook the tagliatelle and courgettes together in lightly salted boiling water until just tender.

Meanwhile, put the soft cheese and 2 tbsp milk in a saucepan and stir over gentle heat until the cheese has melted into a creamy sauce. Add a little extra milk if required. Season with a squeeze of lemon juice and black pepper.

Drain the tagliatelle and courgettes and stir into the sauce. Turn into 2 serving dishes and scatter with the smoked salmon and parsley.

Serve wedges of lemon for squeezing over, if required.

300 12 7 Tagliatelle with Ham, Peas & Crème Fraîche

Serves 1

INGREDIENTS

45g/1½ oz tagliatelle or pasta shapes
2 rounded tbsp frozen peas
45g/1½ oz lean smoked ham, chopped
2 level tbsp half-fat crème fraîche
Black pepper

Cook pasta in lightly salted boiling water until just tender. Add peas to water about 3 minutes before end of cooking time.

Drain pasta and peas and return to pan. Stir in ham and crème fraîche and warm through gently a few seconds, stirring continuously.

Season to taste with black pepper.

300 12 8 Feta Topped Penne

Serves 1

INGREDIENTS

1 small onion, chopped
Spray oil
1 small clove garlic, crushed
1 small green pepper, de-seeded and sliced
  or a good handful frozen mixed sliced peppers
3-4 small fresh or frozen broccoli florets
200g/7 oz canned tomatoes
1 dspn tomato purée
Good pinch Italian seasoning or dried oregano
Salt and black pepper
60g/2 oz penne or other pasta
30g/1 oz feta cheese, cut into small cubes
  or crumbled

Soften onion over gentle heat in pan sprayed with oil. Add garlic and cook 1 minute. Add peppers and broccoli, turn up heat and stir-fry 2-3 minutes.

Stir in tomatoes, tomato purée and herbs. Bring to a gentle simmer and cook approximately 10 minutes. Season to taste.

Cook penne in lightly salted boiling water until just tender. Drain.

Serve penne topped with vegetable sauce and diced or crumbled feta.

Pasta with Herby Sausage Balls

Serves **2**

INGREDIENTS

4 Wall's Lean Recipe sausages*
¼ tsp garlic powder
2 tbsp fresh or frozen chopped parsley
Black pepper
Spray oil
1 small onion, chopped
400g can tomatoes
1 tbsp tomato purée
¼ tsp Italian seasoning or dried oregano
1 tsp heat-stable granulated sweetener
   (e.g. Splenda)
Salt
85g/3 oz pasta shapes

Remove skins from sausages. Mash the sausages together with the garlic powder, chopped parsley and black pepper. Shape into 12 small balls and brown under a pre-heated moderate grill approximately 15-20 minutes, turning frequently.

Soften onion in pan sprayed with oil. Stir in tomatoes, tomato purée, herbs and sweetener. Bring to a simmer and cook 10-15 minutes. Season to taste. Add cooked sausage balls and simmer 5 minutes more.

Cook pasta in lightly salted boiling water until just tender. Drain.

Serve each person with half the pasta topped with half the sausage balls and half the sauce.

* Or other brand very-low-calorie sausage up to 70 calories per sausage.

300 12 2 Turkey & Mushroom Couscous

Serves 1

INGREDIENTS

1 small onion, chopped

Spray oil

100g/3½ oz turkey stir-fry strips

60g/2 oz mushrooms, halved or quartered

200g/7 oz canned tomatoes

1 chicken Oxo cube

2 tbsp water

¼ tsp turmeric

Good pinch of cinnamon

60g/2 oz couscous

Cook onion in pan sprayed with oil until softened and turning golden. If necessary, add 1 tbsp water and cover with a lid for a couple of minutes. Add turkey strips and stir-fry 3-4 minutes.

Add all remaining ingredients except couscous. Bring to a rolling simmer stirring continuously and breaking up the tomatoes.

Stir in couscous, cover pan and turn out heat. (Remove from electric or ceramic hob). Leave for 5-6 minutes until couscous has softened and absorbed the liquid. Fluff up with a fork.

310 12 6 Beef Chow Mein

Serves 2

INGREDIENTS

175g/6 oz lean steak, e.g. rump

4 spring onions

Spray oil

150g/5 oz beansprouts

Handful of shredded savoy cabbage, pak choi or other greens

150g pack Amoy Straight to Wok Noodles

120g sachet Blue Dragon Chow Mein Sauce

Cut the steak into small, thin strips. Slice the spring onions diagonally.

Spray pan or wok with oil and heat. Add the steak and spring onions and stir-fry 2 minutes.

Add the beansprouts, greens and noodles and stir 1 minute, separating the noodles. Add sauce and stir 1 minute more.

Serve half to each person.

per serving

300 12 7 Beef Olives
with Mushrooms

Serves 1

INGREDIENTS

2 x 60 g/2 oz thin slices lean rump steak
   or beef topside, all fat removed
3 level tbsp fresh breadcrumbs
1 tbsp chopped fresh parsley
Grated zest and juice of ½ lemon
1 dspn grated parmesan cheese
Salt and freshly ground black pepper
Spray oil
115 g/4 oz button mushrooms, thinly sliced
3 tbsp marsala wine or medium/sweet sherry
60 ml/2 fl oz beef stock

Flatten out the beef slices with a rolling pin, so you have 2 large squares.

Mix together the breadcrumbs, parsley, lemon zest and juice and parmesan, and season lightly with salt and pepper.

Divide the breadcrumb mixture between the 2 beef slices, then fold the sides over the mixture and roll up into cylinders. Secure with wooden cocktail sticks.

Spray a frying pan lightly with oil and cook the beef olives, turning occasionally, until they are lightly browned all over. Add the mushrooms and cook for 2-3 minutes until golden.

Pour in the marsala or sherry and beef stock and leave to simmer gently for about 15 minutes until the beef is cooked and the liquid has reduced almost to a glaze.

Serve hot with a selection of steamed No-Check vegetables.

305 12 11 Baked Greek Lamb

Serves 1

INGREDIENTS

150 g/5 oz small new potatoes, halved
2 cherry or small plum tomatoes, halved
½ red pepper, deseeded and cut into chunks
1 small aubergine, sliced
1 small onion, sliced
Sprigs of rosemary and oregano
Salt and freshly ground black pepper
Spray olive oil
2 small lamb chops, all fat removed

Pre-heat the oven to 200°C/gas mark 6.

Prepare all the vegetables and place them in a shallow roasting pan. Tuck in the herb sprigs and season with salt and pepper.

Spray lightly with a spritz of oil and then bake for about 20 minutes.

Place the lamb chops on top of the vegetables and return to the oven for about 25 minutes until the chops are browned and cooked to your liking.

300 12 6 Curry Pie

Serves 1

INGREDIENTS

1 small onion, chopped
1 garlic clove, crushed
Spray oil
1 level tbsp curry powder, or to taste
100 g/3½ oz less-than-5%-fat beef mince
1 tbsp tomato purée
200 ml/⅓ pint beef stock
2-3 cauliflower florets, chopped small
1 carrot, thinly sliced
1 rounded tbsp frozen peas
200 g/7 oz potatoes, peeled
Pinch of garam masala (optional)

Cook the onion and garlic until softened in a saucepan that has been sprayed with oil.

Add the curry powder and cook over gentle heat 1 minute, stirring continuously. Add the mince and stir-fry until browned.

Stir in the tomato purée and cook 1 minute. Add the stock, cauliflower, carrots and frozen peas. Bring to a simmer, cover the pan and cook about 20 minutes, until the vegetables are tender.

Meanwhile, boil the potatoes and, when cooked, drain off most of the liquid leaving 2 or 3 tbsp in the pan. Mash the potatoes.

Transfer the curried mince to a heatproof dish. Spread the mashed potato over the top and fork up. Sprinkle with garam masala, if using.

Brown the pie under a pre-heated hot grill.

Microwave Meatloaf & Mash Serves 4

INGREDIENTS

75g/2½ oz small onion, chopped
75g/2½ oz carrot, coarsely grated
400g/14 oz lean minced beef
1 dspn Worcester sauce
1 dspn tomato purée
1 dspn dried parsley
2 Bovril cubes
1 egg, beaten
600g/1¼ lb potatoes
4 dspn low-fat gravy granules (e.g. Oxo or Bisto Best)
No-Check vegetables to serve

nb:

The meatloaf is also good eaten cold with salad.

One-quarter of the loaf alone is 175 cals, 7 Checks, 8 fat.

Peel and boil potatoes and when cooked mash with some of the cooking liquid.

Place onions and carrots in a 1 litre/2 pint microwavable, covered casserole dish. Microwave on high 3½-4 minutes or until soft. Mix in mince, Worcester sauce, tomato purée and parsley. Crumble in stock cubes, add beaten egg and mix thoroughly. Press down mixture and cover.

Microwave on medium (approximately 500 watts) 12 minutes. Stand 5 minutes, then drain off surplus fat.

Make up gravy with 300ml/½ pint boiling water.

Serve one-quarter of the meatloaf, potatoes and gravy to each person with your choice of no-Check vegetables.

Leek Bake

 Serves 4

Courtesy of class member Frances Mair

INGREDIENTS

- 4 medium leeks (or 2 if very long)
- 8 thin slices smoked ham
- 450 ml/¾ pint skimmed milk
- 4 level dspn cornflour
- Salt and pepper
- Knob of low-fat spread
- 115 g/4 oz mature half-fat cheddar, grated
- 3 medium slices bread, made into breadcrumbs
- 8 rounded tbsp peas

Pre-heat oven to 200°C/gas mark 6.

Top and tail the leeks, cut lengthwise and wash thoroughly to remove any grit. If using 2 long leeks, cut each half in two so you have 8 pieces. Place on a plate, cover and microwave until fairly soft.

Wrap a slice of ham around each leek and place in a suitable ovenproof dish (2 rows of 4 make it easier to divide for serving).

Put the cornflour into a saucepan and stir in a little of the milk to dissolve cornflour. Add remaining milk and heat, stirring continuously, until the sauce thickens. Season to taste, and pour white sauce over the leeks and ham.

Melt the low fat spread for a few seconds in the microwave and mix together with the breadcrumbs and grated cheese. Scatter the mixture over the white sauce.

Bake in pre-heated oven 30-40 minutes until cheese and breadcrumbs are golden.

Boil or microwave the peas and serve with the bake.

per serving
300 12 4 Spicy Chickpeas & Couscous

Serves

INGREDIENTS

1 small onion, chopped
Spray oil
1 clove garlic, crushed
Pinch cumin
Pinch cinnamon
½ tsp turmeric
1 small carrot, sliced thinly
200ml/7 fl.oz chicken or vegetable stock
1 courgette, sliced
1 tomato, chopped
4 ready-to-eat apricots, halved
4 tbsp canned chickpeas
45g/1½ oz couscous

Soften onion in a medium saucepan sprayed with oil. Add garlic and spices and cook 1 minute stirring. Add carrots and stock, bring back to a simmer, cover and cook 10 minutes, checking occasionally.

Add courgettes, tomatoes, apricots and chickpeas. Bring back to a simmer and cook 5-10 minutes covered, stirring now and again, until courgettes are just tender.

Push vegetables to one side of the pan and stir couscous into juices. Cover, remove from heat and allow to stand 5 minutes.

Fluff couscous with a fork before serving. If dish is too dry, stir in a little boiling water.

per serving
300 12 6 Courgette Risotto

Serves

INGREDIENTS

1 medium onion, chopped
Spray oil
1 dspn freshly chopped parsley or other herbs
2 courgettes, diced
2 tomatoes, chopped
75g/2½ oz risotto (arborio) rice
275ml/½ pint vegetable stock
2 dspn grated parmesan cheese

Sauté onion in pan sprayed with oil until softened but not browned. Add a little water now and again if necessary to prevent sticking. Add herbs, courgettes, tomatoes and rice.

Whilst continually stirring, add the stock a little at a time, allowing the rice to absorb the liquid before adding more. Continue until the rice is "al dente". Rice should be creamy rather than dry, so add a little more hot water or stock if necessary.

Serve sprinkled with parmesan cheese and additional chopped herbs, if liked.

Low-Check
Desserts

50 **2 0** Golden Fruit Kebabs

Serves 4

or "No-Check" using 1 serving of fruit from Every Day Bonus

INGREDIENTS

4 bamboo skewers
1 eating apple
1 nectarine or peach
2 tangerines, satsumas or clementines
8 fresh or canned in juice pineapple cubes
4 pinches cinnamon or mixed spice

Soak bamboo skewers in water about 15 minutes to prevent scorching.

Core apple and cut into 8 wedges. Stone nectarine or peach (you may prefer to peel peach) and cut into 8 wedges. Peel tangerines and separate into 8 pieces of about 2-3 segments each.

Divide the fruit into 4 equal quantities and arrange on skewers. Sprinkle with spice and cook approximately 4-5 minutes per side under a pre-heated hot grill.

25 **1** 0 Peppered Strawberries

per serving

Serves 2

or "No-Check" using ½ serving of fruit from Every Day Bonus

225g/8 oz strawberries
Black pepper

Hull strawberries and cut in half. Sprinkle with black pepper to taste. Serve as a starter or dessert.

---

per serving

50 **2** 0 Spiced Apple

Serves 1

or "No-Check" using 1 serving of fruit from Every Day Bonus

1 eating apple
Good pinch mixed spice

Cut apple into quarters, remove core, then cut each quarter into 5 thin slices.

Arrange slices in overlapping circles around a small microwavable tea-plate. Sprinkle with mixed spice.

Microwave on high approximately 2 minutes.

---

per serving

45 **2** 0 Cinnamon Plums

Serves 1

or "No-Check" using 1 serving of fruit from Every Day Bonus

3 plums
Good pinch of cinnamon

Cut plums in half and place in a microwavable dish. Sprinkle with cinnamon, cover and microwave on high approximately 2 minutes. Stones are easily removed after cooking.

55 **2** 0 Red Hot Grapefruit

Serves 2

20 **1** 0 *using 1 serving of fruit from Every Day Bonus*

INGREDIENTS

1 large ruby or pink grapefruit
2 tsp brown sugar

Pre-heat grill to moderate.

Cut grapefruit in half and loosen sections by cutting between membranes. Sprinkle each half with 1 tsp brown sugar. Grill approximately 3-5 minutes until sugar melts and grapefruit is warmed through.

Remove carefully from grill and serve warm.

---

80 **3** 0 Brandied Apricots

Serves 3

20 **1** 0 *using 1 average serving of fruit from Every Day Bonus*

INGREDIENTS

411g can apricot halves in fruit juice
Zest from ½ a small unwaxed lemon
1 dspn lemon juice
1-2 tbsp granulated sweetener
2 tbsp brandy or cream sherry

Place apricots with fruit juice, lemon zest and lemon juice into a saucepan. Heat through. Use a slotted spoon to remove apricots. Keep warm.

Boil juices 2 minutes to reduce. Remove pan from heat and allow to come off the boil. Stir in granulated sweetener thoroughly, then stir in brandy or sherry. Pour juice over apricots. Best served warm.

Serve one-third of the recipe to each person.

per serving
70 | 3 | 0 | Honeyed Figs
20 | 1 | 0 | *using 1 average serving of fruit from Every Day Bonus*

Serves **1**

INGREDIENTS

2 fresh figs
1 tsp runny honey

Cut figs in half from stalk to base.

Place on grill rack and drizzle with honey.

Grill under moderate heat until fruits soften and honey bubbles.

---

per serving
50 | 2 | 0 | Apple Snow

Serves **2**

or "No-Check" using 1 average serving of fruit from Every Day Bonus

INGREDIENTS

300g/10 oz cooking apples, peeled, cored and chopped
2 tbsp water
2 tbsp granulated sweetener, or to taste
2 medium egg whites (see note below)

Gently stew the apples in the water, or microwave in a suitable covered dish, until soft. Allow to cool.

Add the sweetener, transfer to a blender and whizz until smooth. Turn out into a large bowl using a spatula to scrape down the sides of the blender.

Beat egg whites until they stand up in peaks and fold gently into the apples using a metal spoon.

Divide between 2 serving dishes.

nb:

This recipe contains raw egg white. Although Lion Quality eggs have been shown to be virtually salmonella-free, it is still recommended that pregnant women, babies and young children, the elderly or anyone with a compromised immune system should avoid raw or undercooked eggs.

variations:

Top each serving with 1 swirl (about the size of an ice cream scoop) half-fat aerosol dairy cream.

per serving
25 | 1 | 2 |

ov

Top each serving with cream as above, plus 1 tsp chocolate vermicelli

per serving
45 | 2 | 3 |

per serving
160 **6** **1** Quick Strawberry Trifle

Serves **1**

INGREDIENTS

1 trifle sponge
50g/about 4-5 strawberries, quartered
1 tsp granulated sweetener
125g pot diet strawberry yoghurt

Cut trifle sponge into 8 small cubes.

Sprinkle the strawberries with the sweetener and leave 10 minutes.

Put half the sponge and half the strawberries into a glass or serving dish. Top with one-third of the yoghurt.

Repeat with remaining ingredients, using all remaining yoghurt and reserving 1 piece of strawberry for decoration.

---

per serving
70 **3** **0** Quick Pears in Wine
20 **1** **0** *using 1 serving of fruit from Every Day Bonus*

INGREDIENTS

1 good-size pear
4 whole cloves
1 tsp heat-stable granulated sweetener
(e.g. Splenda)
1 dspn white wine

Peel pear. Cut into quarters and remove core. Arrange on a microwavable tea-plate core side down. Spike 1 clove into the thick end of each quarter. Sprinkle over sweetener and white wine.

Microwave on high approximately 2 minutes or until pear is tender. Timing will depend on ripeness of pear and power of microwave.

Serve warm, or allow to cool, refrigerate and serve chilled.

50 2 2 Frothy Milk Jelly

Serves 4

or "No-Check" using 1 serving of milk from Every Day Bonus

INGREDIENTS

170g small can "light" evaporated milk (e.g. Carnation Light)
1 sachet sugar-free jelly crystals
400ml/⅔ pint boiling water

Place evaporated milk in fridge at least 4 hours to chill.

Place jelly crystals into a large bowl and pour on boiling water. Stir thoroughly to dissolve crystals. Allow to cool down.

Pour chilled evaporated milk into another large bowl and, using slow to medium speed, whisk until thick and frothy and more than double in volume.

Spoon milk into cooled jelly and whisk slowly. When cool enough, chill in fridge to set. It should separate into three layers.

---

75 3 0 Grown-up Jelly with Summer Fruits

Serves 4

25 1 0 *using 1 serving of fruit from Every Day Bonus*

INGREDIENTS

1 sachet sugar-free jelly crystals
450ml/¾ pint boiling water
1 glass wine
500g bag/carton frozen summer fruits or
450g/1 lb fresh fruit, e.g. strawberries, raspberries, peaches

Place jelly crystals into a bowl and pour on boiling water. Stir thoroughly to dissolve crystals. Stir in wine. Allow to cool, then chill until set.

Allow fruits to defrost, if using frozen, or prepare fresh fruit.

Serve each person with one-quarter of the jelly accompanied by one-quarter of the prepared fruits.

variation:

Use any colour wine with red jellies. Use white wine with citrus flavoured jellies.

50 **2 0** Jelly with Orange Cream

Serves 4

INGREDIENTS

1 sachet sugar-free orange jelly crystals
250g tub quark skimmed milk soft cheese
2 tbsp granulated sweetener (or to taste)
2-3 drops vanilla essence or extract
Juice from ½ orange
Finely grated/zested peel from ½ orange (no pith)

Dissolve jelly crystals in 275ml/½ pint boiling water, then make up to 550ml/1 pint with cold water. Allow to cool, but not to set.

When cool, pour jelly into 4 serving glasses or dishes. Put in a cool place to set jelly.

Lightly beat quark and thoroughly mix in the sweetener, vanilla, orange juice and half the orange zest.

Divide the mixture between the 4 jellies, putting a large swirl on each, and decorate with remaining zest.

If preparing in advance, make up jellies and orange cream separately. Stir cream and put onto jellies just before serving.

per serving
75 **3** **0** Lemon Custard

Serves **1**

20 **1** **0** *using 1 serving of milk from Every Day Bonus*

INGREDIENTS

1 rounded dspn custard powder
150ml/¼ pint skimmed milk
2.5cm/1 inch piece of lemon peel
1-2 tsp granulated sweetener

Put custard powder into a small microwavable jug. Stir in a little of the milk to make a smooth cream. Stir in remaining milk. Add lemon peel.

Microwave on high 45 seconds. Stir and return to microwave 30 seconds. Continue microwaving in 10-15 second bursts, stirring in between, until custard has thickened. Timing depends on coldness of milk and power of microwave.

Stir in granulated sweetener to taste and remove lemon peel before serving.

---

per serving
130 **5** **3** Alaska Special

Serves **4**

INGREDIENTS

2 large egg whites
3 tbsp heat-stable granulated
  sweetener (e.g. Splenda)
1 medium banana, thinly sliced
500ml tub, or half of 1 litre tub, low-
  calorie ice cream
  in chocolate and/or vanilla flavour
  (e.g. Carte d'Or Light)
1 tbsp brandy or cream sherry

Pre-heat oven to 220°C/gas mark 8.

Whisk egg whites to form stiff peaks. Fold in granulated sweetener.

Spread banana slices over the base of an ovenproof plate. Place ice cream on top of banana.

With a small sharp knife, make a few deep slits in the top of the ice cream and sprinkle in the brandy or cream sherry.

Cover ice cream completely with egg white, making sure it is completely sealed. Don't worry if the odd banana slice pokes out, but there shouldn't be any gaps over the ice cream.

Place in hot oven and cook approximately 4-5 minutes, until meringue is golden. Serve immediately.

Serve one-quarter of the recipe to each person.

per serving
155 6 4 Berry Treat

Serves 1

INGREDIENTS

100 g/3½ oz fresh raspberries
100 g/3½ oz fresh strawberries,
   hulled and sliced
Granulated sweetener,
   to taste (optional)
100 g/3½ oz low-fat fresh or
   long-life custard
55 ml swirl (ice-cream scoop size)
   half-fat aerosol cream
Sprig of mint

Put the raspberries and strawberries in a pretty glass bowl. Sweeten if wished with granulated sweetener.

Pour the custard over the fruit to cover it and put in the fridge to chill.

Just before serving, top with a swirl of half-fat cream and decorate with a sprig of mint.

---

per serving
50 2 0 Peach Sorbet

Serves 4

or "No-Check" using 1 serving of fruit from Every Day Bonus

Inspired by Sue Kreitzman

INGREDIENTS

4 large ripe peaches
4 tbsp skimmed milk
4 tbsp granulated sweetener

Peel and stone peaches. Cut each half into 4 chunks. Place chunks on a tray or plate and open-freeze. Once chunks are frozen, transfer to a freezer bag and store in freezer until you are ready to use them.

To use, take out 8 chunks for each person and process or liquidise until well broken down. Hold onto your machine as it clatters a lot! If using a liquidiser, it's best to do one serving at a time.

Add milk and granulated sweetener (1 tbsp of each if doing just one serving). Continue processing until a smooth sorbet consistency is reached. Stop now and again and use a knife to scrape sides and break up chunks. It's still nice with a few chunky pieces left in.

Serve immediately.

tip:
If peaches are difficult to peel, score in quarters through to the stone. Place in a bowl, cover with boiling water and leave 1 minute. Skin should peel off easily.

INGREDIENTS

410 g can pear halves in juice
1 small fluted sponge flan case
200 g/7 oz quark skimmed milk soft cheese
2 tbsp granulated sweetener
Few drops vanilla extract or essence
1 sachet low-calorie chocolate drink
  (e.g. Options Belgian Chocolate)
1 tsp chopped nuts

Drain the pears, reserving 1 tbsp of the juice. Sprinkle the reserved juice over the indent of the flan.

Add the sweetener and vanilla to the quark and beat lightly to mix well.

Spread the mixture over the indent of the flan case.

Arrange the pear halves over the quark, cut side down.

Mix the chocolate drink powder with 1-2 tbsp hot water and stir to make a fairly thick sauce. If necessary, add a few drops more water. Spoon the chocolate sauce over the pears.

Place the nuts on a heatproof plate and toast under the grill until golden – take care to watch them continuously, as they can easily burn! Scatter the toasted nuts over the chocolate pears.

Chill 1 hour before serving, but can be made a day in advance.

90 4 0 Sultana Rice Pudding

Serves 4

INGREDIENTS

45g/1½ oz pudding rice
450ml/¾ pint skimmed milk
2 tbsp heat-stable granulated sweetener
(e.g. Splenda)
1 tbsp sultanas
Freshly grated nutmeg

Pre-heat oven to 150°C/gas mark 2.

Put rice into an ovenproof casserole. Stir in milk, sweetener and sultanas. Sprinkle with freshly grated nutmeg.

Cover tightly and cook in oven approximately 2 hours. (If lid is loose, cover with foil before putting on lid.)

Stir and ideally leave to stand covered, about half an hour, before serving. Or, equally good served chilled the next day.

150 6 1 Apricot Rice Pudding

Serves 2

INGREDIENTS

Smear of low-fat spread for greasing
300 ml/½ pint skimmed milk
30 g/1 oz pudding rice
1 tbsp caster sugar
1 stick cinnamon
Freshly grated nutmeg
4 fresh apricots, halved and stoned
Granulated sweetener, to taste

Pre-heat the oven to 150°C/gas mark 2.

Pour the skimmed milk into a lightly greased ovenproof baking dish. Add the pudding rice, sugar and cinnamon stick. Grate some fresh nutmeg over the top.

Place the dish in the pre-heated low oven and cook very gently for about 2 hours, until the rice swells and absorbs the liquid, and you have a creamy pudding.

Cook the apricots in a pan with a little water and granulated sweetener, to taste, over a gentle heat until softened to a thick purée.

Serve the rice pudding hot or cold with the apricot purée on top.

150 6 3 Orange Meringues

Serves

INGREDIENTS

1½ tbsp cornflour
75 ml/2½ fl oz water
Grated zest and juice of
  1 large juicy orange
2 tbsp caster sugar
1 egg, separated

Blend the cornflour with the water until smooth and there are no lumps. Add the orange zest and juice and heat in a pan, stirring all the time with a wooden spoon, until the orange mixture thickens.

Remove the pan from the heat and sweeten with half the caster sugar. Set aside and when cool, beat in the egg yolk.

Spoon the orange mixture into 2 small heatproof glass or ramekin dishes and bake in a pre-heated oven at 180°C/gas mark 4 for about 5 minutes.

Whisk the egg white until stiff and then beat in the rest of the caster sugar, a teaspoonful at a time, until the mixture is glossy and stands in stiff peaks.

Spoon the meringue onto the orange mixture and bake for a further 5-10 minutes until the meringue is slightly tinged with brown.

160 6 0 Summer Fruit Brûlée

per serving

Serves

INGREDIENTS

115 g/4 oz fresh berries,
  e.g. raspberries,
  strawberries,
  redcurrants
1 medium peach, skinned,
  stoned and diced
3 rounded tbsp virtually
  fat-free fromage frais
1 tsp demerara sugar

Put the berries and diced peach into a small heatproof dish.

Spoon the fromage frais over the berries and level the top. Pop into the fridge for about 10 minutes to chill and firm up the fromage frais.

Meanwhile, heat the grill until it is really hot.

Sprinkle the sugar evenly over the top of the chilled fromage frais to cover the surface, and then pop under the pre-heated grill.

Watch carefully and don't go away and forget the dessert or it will burn! When the sugar melts evenly and caramelizes, remove it immediately. Allow to cool before eating. (Note that, if you have one, you can use a blow torch instead of grilling).

Mango & Ginger Filo Stacks

Serves **2**

INGREDIENTS

2 x 15 g/½ oz sheets filo pastry
1 small egg, beaten
250 g/9 oz ripe mango
1 small knob stem ginger plus 1 teaspoon syrup
Icing sugar, for dusting
Cocoa powder, for dusting

Pre-heat oven to 200°C/gas mark 6.

Brush each sheet of filo pastry lightly with the beaten egg and then fold in half widthwise before brushing with more beaten egg. Cut each sheet in half so you have 4 pieces of filo pastry and place on a baking sheet lined with baking parchment.

Cook in a preheated oven for about 10 minutes until the filo sheets are crisp and golden. Remove and cool.

Peel the mango and cut away the flesh from the stone. Slice thinly and set aside. Chop the stem ginger.

Place a sheet of cooked filo pastry on each of 2 serving plates. Top each sheet with the mango and sprinkle with the stem ginger and syrup. Cover with the remaining filo sheets.

Serve immediately with a light dusting of icing sugar and cocoa powder.

Rocky Road Revival

Serves

INGREDIENTS

1 Nestlé Fitnesse chocolate cereal bar
300 ml/½ pint very cold skimmed milk
1 sachet sugar-free chocolate "Delight"
  (e.g. Bird's Angel Delight)

variations:

Make with different flavours of "delight"
(e.g. butterscotch or vanilla or banana) and
cereal bar (up to around 100 calories e.g.
Kellogg's Special K bar).

or

Freeze around 2 hours. If left in the freezer
longer and it goes rock solid, pop in the
microwave for a few seconds before serving
– ideal when just starting to go creamy around
the edges.

or

Top each serving with a 55ml
(ice-cream scoop size) swirl of half-fat
aerosol cream just before serving. Add 1
Check 2g fat per serving.

Cut the cereal bar along its length and then slice
thinly so you have around 20-24 small pieces.

Pour the milk into a glass bowl or jug and sprinkle
over the chocolate powder. Whisk thoroughly,
preferably with a balloon whisk, until completely
dissolved. Leave to thicken 1 minute.

Place about 5-6 pieces of cereal bar into each of 4
small ramekins or small wine glasses. Pour over the
mixture, dividing it equally between the 4 servings
and stirring in the cereal bar pieces. Leave to thicken
a further 2-3 minutes, or chill in the fridge before
serving. (Best not made more than 2 hours before
serving).

Low-Check
Cakes

per serving

120 5 4 Low-Check Carrot & Apricot Cake

Serves 10

INGREDIENTS

2 medium eggs
45g/1½ oz 60% fat olive oil spread
(e.g. Bertolli)
60g/2 oz brown sugar
2 tbsp heat-stable granulated sweetener
(e.g. Splenda)
115g/4 oz finely grated carrot
60g/2 oz ready-to-eat apricots, chopped
115g/4 oz wholemeal self-raising flour

Pre-heat oven to 180°/gas mark 4.

Line a 500g/1 lb loaf tin with baking parchment or Release non-stick foil.

Separate egg whites from yolks and whisk whites until stiff.

Whisk together spread, egg yolks, sugar and sweetener until pale and fluffy. Whisk in grated carrots and chopped apricots and gradually add flour.

Slacken mixture with 1 tbsp of whisked whites, then fold in remaining whites with a metal spoon. Pour mixture into prepared tin, level off and bake approximately 45-60 minutes, until a skewer inserted into the middle comes out clean.

Even better the next day.

Cut into 10 slices. Freezes well.

---

per serving

35 1.5 1.5 Ambassador's Choice

Makes 24

INGREDIENTS

8 Ryvita Multigrain crispbreads
100g/3½ oz chocolate hazelnut spread

Put Ryvitas into a polythene bag and crush quite finely.

Melt chocolate spread in a bowl over a pan of simmering water. Remove bowl from heat and stir in crushed Ryvita crumbs.

Take a teaspoonful of the mixture, pat gently into a ball and place in a paper sweet case. Repeat to make 24.

Chunky Apple & Sultana Loaf

Serves

INGREDIENTS

60 g/2 oz sultanas

2 tbsp apple or orange juice

2 medium eggs

50 g/1¾ oz caster sugar

175 g/6 oz self-raising flour

½ tsp mixed spice

2 tbsp skimmed milk

1 large cooking apple, peeled, cored and cut into small dice

1 small eating apple, peeled, cored and sliced into thin wedges

½ tsp caster sugar

Pre-heat the oven to 180oC/gas mark 4.

Line a 500 g/1 lb loaf tin with baking parchment.

Soak the sultanas in the juice at least 15 minutes.

Place the eggs and sugar in a mixing bowl and, with an electric whisk, whisk together until pale and frothy.

Sift in the flour and mixed spice and mix with a metal spoon. Add the milk to slacken the mixture a little. Stir in the sultanas and any remaining juice and the chopped cooking apple.

Spoon the mixture evenly into the prepared tin and smooth over the top. Overlap the eating apple slices along the length of the tin. Sprinkle the slices with the ½ tsp sugar.

Bake in the centre of the pre-heated oven approximately 45 minutes or until risen and firm to the touch and apple slices are tinged brown. Leave in the tin 5 minutes before removing baking parchment and turning out onto a wire rack to cool.

Store in an airtight container 2-3 days, or cut in slices and freeze to store longer.

145 6 2 No-Added-Fat Sponge

Serves 8

2 medium eggs
115g/4 oz caster sugar
115g/4 oz self-raising flour
5 level tbsp reduced-sugar jam
1 tsp icing sugar

nb:

Unfilled sponge can be used as the base for fruit-filled or topped gateaux, or just served with fruit and/or ice cream. (Add Checks as appropriate.)

Sponge alone, per one-eighth serving 125 cals, 5 Checks, 2 fat.

Pre-heat oven to 180°C/gas mark 4.

Line a 20cm/8 inch loose-bottom cake tin with non-stick foil (e.g. BacoFoil Release).

Put eggs and sugar into a bowl and with an electric whisk, whisk until pale, thick and creamy.

Sift flour into the bowl and fold into eggs and sugar mix. Turn mix into the cake tin and bake just above centre of oven approximately 30 minutes or until firm to the touch.

Leave in tin 5 minutes, then turn out onto a wire rack to cool.

Split sponge horizontally through the centre and spread with the reduced-sugar jam. Sift icing sugar over the top.

---

120 5 4 Sultana Scones

Makes 12

225g/8 oz plain flour
Pinch of salt
1 tsp baking powder
100g/3½ oz low-fat spread
2 level tbsp sugar
30g/1 oz sultanas
1 medium egg
3 tbsp skimmed milk
Skimmed milk to glaze

Pre-heat oven to 200°C/gas mark 6.

Sift flour, salt and baking powder into a bowl. Rub in the low-fat spread until it resembles breadcrumbs. Stir in the sugar and sultanas.

Beat the egg with the 3 tbsp milk. Gradually add to the dry mixture and mix to a soft dough.

Turn out onto a lightly floured surface and roll out to 1cm/½ inch thickness. Cut out 12 rounds using a 5cm/2 inch cutter and place on a lightly oil-sprayed baking sheet. Alternatively, cover baking sheet with non-stick foil (e.g. BacoFoil Release).

Brush the tops with a little skimmed milk and bake approximately 15-20 minutes until a light golden colour. Transfer to a wire rack to cool.

150 6 4 Prune & Apple Muffins

Serves 10

INGREDIENTS

100g/3½ oz self-raising white flour
100g/3½ oz self-raising wholemeal flour
½ tsp baking powder
2 tbsp heat-stable granulated sweetener
40g/1½ oz sugar
175ml/6 fl.oz skimmed milk
2 medium eggs
2 tbsp sunflower or vegetable oil
1 apple, peeled and diced
60g/2 oz ready-to-eat prunes, chopped

Pre-heat oven to 200°C/gas mark 6.

Place 10 muffin cases in a muffin pan or deep bun tin, or on a baking tray (but they won't hold their shape as well if not supported at the sides).

Sift the flours, baking powder and sweetener into a bowl, then stir in the wholemeal bran left in the sieve. Stir in the sugar.

Beat the milk, eggs and oil together well. Make a well in the flour and pour in the liquid. Beat lightly until just mixed. Do not over-beat. Fold in the apples and prunes and spoon mixture into the muffin cases.

Bake approximately 25 minutes until well risen. Put muffins on a wire rack to cool. (If you peel off the paper case too soon, half the muffin will stick to the bottom!).

Best eaten the same day, but can be frozen. Either allow to defrost about 1 hour, or pop frozen muffin in the microwave around 30-45 seconds.

Essential
Extras

Just One Check!

1 satsuma or tangerine	1	0
2 small plums	1	0
3 small semi-dried apricots	1	0
Freeze 40g/1-½ oz grapes - suck slowly when frozen!	1	0
1 supermarket "fun-size" (children's lunchbox) apple	1	0
Stuff 1 tomato with 1 tbsp cottage cheese	1	1
Fill 25cm/10 inch stick of celery with 1 Laughing Cow Light Cheese Triangle - then cut into 10 pieces!	1	1
Top 1 Ryvita Original or Dark Rye Crispbread or 1 rice-cake with tomato/cucumber slices and/or a scraping of Marmite	1	0
Dip no-Check vegetable strips into 1 tbsp (about 25-30g/1 oz) Philadelphia Extra Light Soft Cheese or Sainsbury's Be Good To Yourself Low Fat Soft Cheese.	1	1
2 wafer-thin slices ham, chicken or turkey plus no-Check salad	1	1

Low on Checks and feel like a snack? Each of the following ideas will cost you just one Check!

2 shredded seafood sticks sprinkled with a few drops soy sauce plus no-Check salad	1	1
1 Wall's strawberry, chocolate or vanilla Mini Milk Lolly	1	1
Unlimited sugar-free jelly with 55ml (ice-cream scoop size) swirl Anchor Light Aerosol Dairy Cream	1	2
60g/2 oz raspberries or chopped strawberries with 30ml/2 level tbsp Anchor Light Aerosol Dairy Cream	1	1
7g/about a handful Puffed Wheat	1	0
7g/about a handful Rice Krispies	1	0
1 rich tea finger biscuit	1	1
1 sponge finger	1	0
1 Doria Amaretti biscuit	1	0.5
1 Cremosa Chupa Chups Sugar-free Lolly	1	0.5

Essential
Extras

For a Couple of Checks

Grilled tomatoes or mushrooms on 1 small slice toast.	2	0.5
1 Ryvita Original or Dark Rye spread with 1 Laughing Cow Light cheese triangle.	2	1
30 g/1 oz thinly sliced cooked lean meat with as much No-Check salad as you want.	2	2
2 seafood sticks with 1 tsp sweet chilli sauce.	2	0
Coarsely grate a large carrot. Sprinkle with lemon juice and pepper and scatter with 1 dspn sunflower or pumpkin seeds.	2	4
Mix 45 g/1½ oz cooked weight, cold pasta with chopped tomato, cucumber and spring onion and sprinkle with balsamic vinegar or oil-free dressing.	2	0.5
Celery sticks with 30 g/1 oz less-than-3% fat cheddar or 50 g/1¾ oz extra light soft cheese.	2	2
1 sachet of low-calorie cup soup.	2	1.5
1 Jumbo Snack-a-Jack	2	0.5
10-15g pack Sainsbury's Be Good To Yourself Bacon Waffles, Onion Rings or Salt & Vinegar Fries.	2	0
1 apple or orange or peach or pear or 2 rings canned (in juice) pineapple	2	0
100ml small glass of apple or cranberry or grapefruit or mango or orange or pineapple juice	2	0

Core a small 100g/3½ oz Cox's apple and cut into 12 wedges. Arrange around a microwavable plate, scatter with 10 sultanas and a pinch of mixed spice or a couple of cloves. Microwave on high 2 minutes	2	0
Spread 1 tsp reduced-sugar jam on 1 rice cake and top with a few berries or slices of fruit.	2	0
Sugar-free jelly with 1 level scoop plain ice cream.	2	2
1 Iceland orange juice lolly	2	0
2 rich tea finger or marie biscuits	2	2
1 sachet of low-calorie hot chocolate drink.	2	1.5
3 Cadbury's mini eggs or 1 Creme Egg Mini, or 1 segment Terry's Chocolate Orange, or 1 Toblerone One by Ones, or 1 average chocolate from a selection box.	2	2.5
25 ml shot of brandy or gin or rum or vodka or whisky – with or without sugar-free mixer!	2	0

No-Check
Vegetables

The vegetables listed on this page have No-Check value so may be used freely on the Positive Eating Plan.

Use to make:

- soups
- salads
- vegetable purées
- sauces
- in stews and casseroles
- in stir-fries
- or finely chopped to extend mince

They may be:

- eaten raw
- boiled
- steamed
- poached in stock
- or microwaved

Or, using a few sprays of low-calorie spray oil, they may be:

- pan-fried or griddled
- roasted
- grilled
- or barbecued

Alfalfa sprouts
Artichoke hearts
Asparagus
Aubergine
Baby sweetcorn
Bamboo shoots
Beansprouts
Beetroot
Bok choi/pak choi
Broccoli
Brussels sprouts
Cabbage, all types
Calabrese
Carrots
Cauliflower
Celeriac
Celery
Chard
Chicory
Chinese leaves
Christophene (cho-cho)
Courgettes
Cress/mustard & cress
Cucumber
Dandelion leaves
Endive
Fennel
French beans (haricots verts)
Green beans
Hearts of palm
Jerusalem artichokes

Kale
Khol rabi
Leeks
Lettuce, all types
Lotus tubers
Mangetout/snow peas
Marrow
Mooli
Mushrooms, all types including exotic
Okra
Onions, all types
Patty pan
Peppers, all colours
Pumpkin
Radishes
Runner beans
Salad leaves, all types
Salsify
Seaweed (not deep fried)
Shallots
Spinach
Spring greens
Squash, all types, e.g. acorn, butternut
Sugar snap peas
Swede
Tomatoes
Turnips
Water chestnuts
Watercress

No-Check
Additions

Artificial sweeteners

Baking powder *

Beef extract *

Chilli peppers

Cream of tartar

Dried vegetables

Egg white

Essences & extracts, e.g. vanilla

Garlic

Gelatine

Herbs, fresh, frozen or dried

Orange flower water

Rhubarb

Root ginger

Rose water

Spices, whole or powdered

Stock cubes */Stock granules */Bouillon *

Sundried tomatoes (not in oil) *

Tomato purée (no added oil)

Spray cooking oil

Sugar-free gum

Sugar-free jelly

Vegetarian gelling powder

Yeast, fresh or dried

Yeast extract *

No-Check
Drinks

Water

Bottled waters up to 3 calories per 100ml

Teas, china or Indian

Teas, fruit or herbal

Diet fizzy drinks up to 3 calories per 100ml

Diet mixers

No-added-sugar low-calorie squashes

No-Check
Dressings
& Sauces

Anchovy essence *	Pepper
Balsamic vinegar	Salt *
Chilli sauce (not sweet)	Shoyu *
Hot pepper sauce	Soy sauce *
Lemon juice/slices	Tamari *
Lime juice/slices	Teriyaki sauce *
Mint sauce	Thai fish sauce (nam pla) *
Mustard *	Vinegar
Mushroom ketchup *	Wine vinegar
Oil-free vinaigrettes	Worcestershire sauce *

nb: An asterisk (*) indicates a high salt content.
Use these items as sparingly as possible.

No-Check
Pickles

Capers *

Cocktail/silverskin onions *

Gherkins *

Jalapenos *

Pickled beetroot *

Pickled mixed vegetables *

Pickled onions *

Pickled red cabbage

Sauerkraut *

Sushi ginger *

Low-Check
Foods

Fish & Seafood

Cod or Coley Fillet, raw, 100g	80	3	1
Crab White Meat, 100g can, drained	45	2	0.5
Haddock or Whiting Fillet, raw 100g	80	3	1
Monkfish, raw, 100g	65	2.5	0.5
Prawns, peeled, cooked, 100g	100	4	1
Seafood Sticks, 2	25	1	0

Meat & Poultry

Beef, cubes, extra lean, raw, 100g	120	5	4
Beef, mince, less than 5% fat, raw, 100g	135	5	5
Beef, rump steak, well trimmed, raw, 100g	125	5	4
Beef, topside, lean only, raw, 100g	115	5	3
Chicken, skinless breast meat, raw, 100g	105	4	1.5
Chicken Livers, raw, 100g	90	4	2.5
Ham with added water, 100g	105	4	4
Kidney, average of all types, raw, 100g	90	4	2.5
Lamb, leg steaks, extra lean, raw, 100g	130	5	5
Pork, escalopes, raw, 100g	100	4	2
Pork, leg, raw, 100g	105	4	2
Turkey, breast meat, raw, 100g	105	4	1
Veal, escalopes, raw, 100g	105	4	2

Recipe Index